THE
STUART
TOWNEND
COLLECTION

Compilation copyright © 2010 Kingsway Communications Ltd
26-28 Lottbridge Drove, Eastbourne, East Sussex, BN23 6NT, United Kingdom
First published 2010, Reprinted 2010, 2011
ISBN 978-1-842913-96-3

Cover design and photography by Andy Colthart (www.jharts.co.uk)

Music setting by David Ball and Paul Hughes

Typesetting and CD-ROM design by Chris Tice

Project co-ordination by Paul Hughes and Phil Johnson

Print production by Scantech Lithographic Ltd

THE STUART TOWNEND COLLECTION

CONTENTS

FOREWORD

Over the years, we have been privileged to host hundreds of young people on our *New Frontiers* training year programmes. It was in that context that I first met Stuart Townend. Since then it has been my great joy and privilege to watch him grow and develop as a hymnwriter, songwriter and worship leader of extraordinary gifting.

His combination of melody and truth has been a delight, and his commitment to provide us with words not merely centred in ourselves and our passing feelings but in God has been magnificent.

He not only has a great grasp of biblical truth and creedal statements but also combines that with a fine sensitivity to the challenges of life that we all face and our need to be settled and secure in all that God has promised. His songs have provided a wonderful ground of confidence to many as they have fully expressed their heartfelt appreciation to God in song.

He has been unflinching in his determination to stay true to biblical revelation, even when some have challenged and urged him to soften the clear statements of Scripture reflected in his songs.

It's been a great joy to often be present when Stuart has introduced one of his new songs to the congregation in Brighton, and I am now fully acquainted with his painstaking attention to detail in their preparation. I am so glad that his songs go around the world so that a whole generation benefits from Stuart's great global impact.

I wish every success to this book with its collection of Stuart's great songs and pray that even more people might be introduced to them.

Terry Virgo

PREFACE

This book collects just about all the worship songs I've written (or co-written) over the last twenty years. People have been asking me for some time if a collection of my songs is available, because up to now the sheet music has been scattered through various hymnals and songbooks, making it difficult (and expensive) to get hold of them all. Although that difficulty has now been overcome to some extent by the availability of sheet music online (via www.kingswaysongs.com), this is still the first time a collection has been made in a paper format.

MY BACKGROUND

I was born in Edinburgh in June 1963. My dad was a Church of the Nazarene pastor, and we moved to Morley, West Yorkshire, when I was six months old. I was the youngest of four boys, and from an early age music was very much part of domestic life. We all had piano lessons, and my dad was self-taught on the piano accordion and harmonica.

Growing up, my attention was divided between Bach, Beethoven and other classical composers, and the Beatles, David Bowie and Stevie Wonder (the latter group almost always winning out). By the time I was a teenager two of my brothers and I had formed a band that played in various churches in the area, and we were writing and performing our own songs on guitars and piano.

By that time my dad had been called into the Anglican ministry, and we had moved first to Kirkheaton, then Sowerby Bridge. Although as a PK ('preacher's kid', for the uninitiated) church had always played a major part in my life, it was only at around thirteen that I came to a personal faith in Christ.

When I was eighteen I began studying at the University of Sussex, Brighton, and joined Clarendon Church, as it was then called (now CCK), having come into a fresh experience of the Spirit in the previous summer. Dave Fellingham encouraged me to get involved in the worship team, first as a keyboard player and then co-leading on guitar with him.

Working alongside Dave was a time of huge growth for me, musically, spiritually, and in terms of understanding the dynamics of congregational worship. I also benefited greatly from the superb, insightful teaching week in week out of preachers like Terry Virgo and John Hosier. (At this time I met and married Caroline, my wonderful wife, and we now have three children: Joseph, Emma and Eden.)

I had also started working for Kingsway Music, where under the encouragement of Les Moir and John Pac I began to have opportunities to play in recording sessions and produce albums, and where I came into contact with many great writers and worship leaders, who taught me so much and to whom I am very grateful.

STONELEIGH

One of the most significant milestones for me in my writing and worship leading was the Stoneleigh Bible Week. Stoneleigh is actually a small village in the heart of England, the site of the UK's National Agricultural Showground, but through the 1990s it hosted the New Frontiers International Bible Week, and became famous around the world for its Bible teaching and worship, which was captured on a live album each year.

These albums contained the best of the new songs from around the world, as well as an increasing number of 'homegrown' songs from Paul Oakley, Nathan Fellingham, Kate Simmonds and myself. The albums became hugely successful throughout the UK and beyond, and undoubtedly helped to launch songs like *How deep the Father's love, Beautiful Saviour* and *In Christ alone*.

It was a fruitful time for me: being able to write with a particular event (and deadline!) looming helped focus the mind, and I was often gripped by the need to write songs on particular subjects that I felt were missing from the church's song repertoire – particularly songs that declared the character of God, and who we are in Christ.

WRITING

I look back on Stoneleigh as a really important and fruitful time for me. But it was as Stoneleigh was drawing to a close, and I met and started working with Keith Getty, that the writing aspect of my work took more centre stage. The story behind our first co-write, *In Christ alone*, and other songs is elsewhere in this book, but I owe a huge debt to Keith not only for his melodic genius and his insightful input into my lyric writing, but for his energy, his tenacity, his encouragement and his great friendship.

Keith and I are from very different church and musical backgrounds, and even hold different theological nuances on many issues – which sometimes makes for interesting songwriting sessions! But we share a passion to see the church of Christ enriched and built up through what it sings, and to see music help draw many to a saving knowledge of Him. As we see it, songs and hymns have a vital role in the following:

1. Putting truths into people's mouths, minds and hearts. The truth of God is the foundation for our lives, and yet I've often struggled to find recent songs that are based on the unchanging truths of who God is, what He has done, and who we are because of Christ. Yes, we need songs that describe the experience of being in God's presence, that express our devotion and commitment to Him; but at the core of worship is considering and declaring *Him*: His attributes, His love, His power, His faithfulness.

2. Telling the story of the gospel. Stories, particularly true stories, are incredibly powerful. The great narratives of the Bible root our faith in historical and present reality. As Christians we don't just embrace a set of concepts; we follow a God who has intervened in history, who has revealed His salvation in flesh and blood, and who interacts with men and women today. And stories are a powerful way of communicating to believers and unbelievers alike the life-changing truth of Christ.

3. Using the power of music and poetry to explore great truths. It's not an accident that large parts of the Bible are written in poetry. It's part of the multitude of artistic gifts God has given us to explore the heights and depths of His glory, and reveal something that mere prose cannot do.

ABOUT THIS BOOK

Unlike most songbooks these days that are arranged alphabetically, this collection is broadly chronological, with each stage of my musical journey being marked by the songs recorded on a particular album. I hope it gives more of a sense of the writing process I have been through – the different musical styles I have wanted to explore, and the different themes and passions that have gripped my heart at various stages of my life.

Many of the arrangements have also been expanded somewhat from the usual songbook format to include introductions and instrumental musical sections (often following the album arrangement), which may help individual musicians and worship teams to develop more interesting arrangements. The *Monument to Mercy* section in particular follows the more complex piano parts to most of the songs played on the album, as many have requested. Also punctuating the book are occasional 'Story behind the song' pieces, explaining why and how a particular song was written.

I hope this book is of use to individuals and teams alike, and helps draw us all into a deeper understanding, appreciation and love for our amazing God.

Stuart Townend
January 2010

SAY THE WORD

Although the studio environment was very familiar to me, the *Say the Word* album was my first proper experience as an 'artist', rather than as a producer or session player. And the experience is quite different! Whereas before I was contributing to someone else's project, now everything was based around my songs, my tastes, my abilities (or lack of them), and was somehow supposed to sound like me – it can be a weird and even scary experience!

Thankfully, on this first album (and all those since) I had a fantastic bunch of musicians around me, and it was exciting to see them at work making songs like *How deep the Father's love* and *How long?* take on new depth and power because of their skills. I learned a huge amount through the experience, and it helped me get used to this new role in the studio. And many of the songs recorded for the first time here in a studio are still used in churches around the world, which is very gratifying.

Lord, how majestic You are
(You are my everything)

Stuart Townend

My first love
(Like a child)

2 Sam 6:14; Ps 42:7; 85:6; Song 8:6;
Mt 24:31; Jn 4:14; 1 Cor 15:52;
1 Thess 4:16;4 Rev 2:4

Stuart Townend

1. My first love is a blaz-ing fi-re, I feel His pow'r-ful love in me; for he has kin-dled a flame of pas-sion, and I will let it grow in me. And in the night I will sing Your praise, my love. And in the morn-ing I'll seek your face, my love.

2. My first love is a rushing river,
   A waterfall that will never cease;
   And in the torrent of tears and laughter,
   I feel a healing power released.
   And I will draw from Your well of life, my love,
   And in Your grace I'll be satisfied, my love.

3. Restore the years of the church's slumber,
   Revive the fire that has grown so dim;
   Renew the love of those first encounters,
   That we may come alive again.
   And we will rise like the dawn throughout the earth,
   Until the trumpet announces Your return.

We have sung our songs of victory

(How long?)

2 Chron 7:14; Ps 68:5;
Is 35:5-6

Stuart Townend

1. We have sung our songs of vic - t'ry, we have prayed to You for rain; we have cried for Your com - pas - sion to re-new the land a-gain. Now we're stand-ing in Your pre - sence, more hun-gry than be-fore; now we're on Your steps of mer - cy, and we're knock-ing at Your door. How long be - fore You

3. But I know a day is com-ing when the
deaf will hear His voice, when the blind will see their Sa-viour, and the
lame will leap for joy. When the wi-dow finds a hus-band who will
al-ways love his bride, and the or-phan finds a fa-ther who will
ne-ver leave her side. How long be-fore Your

glo-ry lights the skies? How long be-fore Your

ra-diance lifts our eyes? How long be-fore Your

fra-grance fills the air? How long be-fore the

earth re-sounds with songs. How long earth re-sounds with songs of

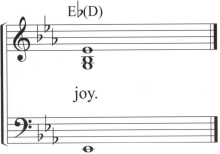

joy.

2. Lord, we know Your heart is broken
By the evil that You see,
And You've stayed Your hand of judgement
For You plan to set men free.
But the land is still in darkness,
And we've fled from what is right;
We have failed the silent children
Who will never see the light.

STORY BEHIND THE SONG
WE HAVE SUNG OUR SONGS OF VICTORY (HOW LONG?)

How long? is probably not the sort of song that gets used every week at church. But the cry of grief about the state of the world, of heartfelt intercession as we wait for God to act, and the hope of ultimate salvation is an aspect of worship that is very biblical and should perhaps feature more in our corporate worship than it does at present.

The song came about as a result of two disparate influences of the time. One was my study of the 'difficult' psalms: not the ones that elicit joyful praise with loud instruments, or marvel at the wonder of creation, but the ones that cry to God from a dark place of sorrow, even anger.

Some of those psalms are quite shocking in their expression of raw emotion, challenging God to act in difficult situations. Is it really OK to address God like that?

And yet the more I think about it, the more I see it as part of the profound mystery of prayer; the invitation to share in the sense of injustice, pain and sorrow that pervades our world, and to cry with all our hearts for a change, knowing that one day God will fulfil His word and put an end to the power of sin and death.

The other influence was rather less sacred! There are albums that move me deeply, and Peter Gabriel's *So* recording was one of those at the time. Tracks like *Mercy Street* and *Don't give up* are achingly beautiful, and stirred something in me that resulted in this song.

I have heard
(I won't let go)

Gen 32:24,26; Mt 7:7
Lk 6:35; 11:9; 1 Cor 13:5

Stuart Townend

Verse

1. I have heard that You are swift to bless the seek-er,
As Ja-cob wres - tled so I'll wres - tle with Your an-gel,

and I be-lieve that You will hear the con-stant cry;
and though I'm wea - ry, I will not be o - ver-come,

so I will call un-til I know I've had an an - swer,
for You have giv - en me a pas - sion for Your king-dom,

I need Your pow er, Lord!
O let Your glo - ry fall!

I won't let

2. I have heard that You show mercy to a nation,
   And I believe that You give power to Your church;
   So now I'm asking You to open up the heavens,
   Pour out Your mercy, Lord!
   For Your gospel to be lived among Your people,
   For Your miracle of healing on the streets;
   For the government to fear the Lord Almighty,
   We need Your power, Lord!

3. For a hunger that will overcome my weakness,
   For a love that will seek its own reward;
   For my life to make a difference in this nation,
   I need Your power, Lord!

The King of love
(The King has come)

Song 6:3; 7:9; Is 61:1; Lk 4:18;
Jn 20:25-27; Rev 1:14-18; 5:9

Stuart Townend & Kevin Jamieson

Capo 3 (D)

♩ = 125

15

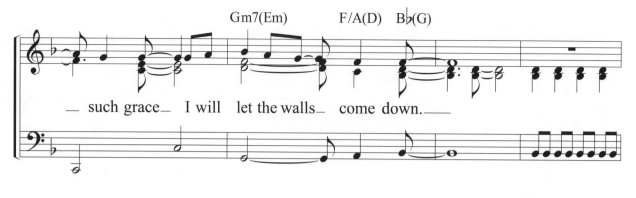

such grace I will let the walls come down.

And I

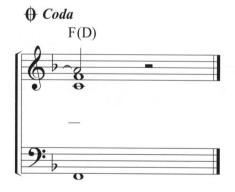

2. My Lover's breath is sweetest wine,
   I am His prize, and He is mine;
   How can a sinner know such joy?
   Because of Jesus.
   The wounds of love are in His hands,
   The price is paid for sinful man;
   Accepted child, forgiven son,
   Because of Jesus.

STORY BEHIND THE SONG
HOW DEEP THE FATHER'S LOVE

Writing this song was an unusual experience for me. I'd already written quite a few songs for worship, but all in a more contemporary worship style, drawing from my own musical background. But I distinctly remember getting this feeling one day that I was going to write a hymn! Now, like most people, I am familiar with hymns – they form part of my church background and I love the truth contained in many of them – but I don't go home at the end of a busy day and put on a hymns album! So I don't think of hymns as where I'm at musically at all.

Nevertheless, I'd been meditating on the cross, and in particular what it cost the Father to give up His beloved Son to a torturous death on a cross. And what was my part in it? Not only was it my sin that put him there, but if I'd lived at that time, I probably would have been among that crowd, shouting with everyone else, 'Crucify Him!' It just makes his sacrifice all the more personal, all the more amazing, and all the more humbling.

As I was thinking through this, I just began to sing the melody, and it flowed in the sort of way that makes you think you've stolen it from somewhere! So the melody was pretty instant, but the words took quite a bit of reworking, as I tried to make every line as strong as I could.

After it was finished, I remember playing it to Dave Fellingham a few minutes before a time of worship. I was worried it was perhaps too twee, too predictable. Dave, in his typical demonstrative and over-enthusiastic way, shrugged his shoulders and said, 'Yeah, it's good', and that was that. It was only when I began to use it in worship, and all sorts of people of different ages and backgrounds responded to it so positively, that I thought it might be a useful resource to the church at large.

Now I'm finding it gets used all over the world, by all sorts of churches; it seems to be as accessible to a traditional church as it is to a house church, and I'm excited by that. But it has perhaps branded me as an old man before my time. It was fed back to me that at a conference a couple who loved the song were surprised to hear I was still alive...

How deep the Father's love for us

Capo 2 (D)

Ps 22:1; Mt 20:28; 27:46;
Mk 10:45; 15:34; Lk 23:35; Jn 3:16; 19:30;
Gal 6:14; 1 Tim 2:6; Heb 2:10; 1 Pet 2:24

Stuart Townend

♩ = 103

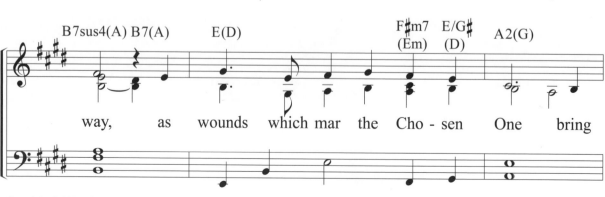

1. How deep the Fa-ther's love for us, how vast be-yond all mea - sure, that He should give His on - ly Son to make a wretch His trea - sure. How great the pain of sear-ing loss, the Fa - ther turns His face a - way, as wounds which mar the Cho - sen One bring

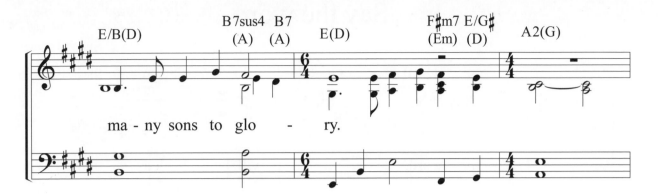

ma - ny sons to glo - ry.

2. Behold the man upon a cross,
   My sin upon His shoulders;
   Ashamed, I hear my mocking voice
   Call out among the scoffers.
   It was my sin that held Him there
   Until it was accomplished;
   His dying breath has brought me life -
   I know that it is finished.

3. I will not boast in anything,
   No gifts, no power, no wisdom;
   But I will boast in Jesus Christ,
   His death and resurrection.
   Why should I gain from His reward?
   I cannot give an answer,
   But this I know with all my heart,
   His wounds have paid my ransom.

Say the word

Is 53:11; Hos 6:3; Joel 2:23; Mt 5:5-6; 8:8;
Lk 7:7; Jn 4:14; 2 Cor 8:9; 12:9; Phil 1:6

Stuart Townend

Capo 1 (D)

1. Say the word, I will be healed; You are the great Phy-si-cian, You meet ev-ry need. Say the word, I will be free; where chains have held me cap-tive, come sing Your songs to me, say the word.

2. Say the word, I will be filled; You my hands reach out to hea-ven, where stri-ving is stilled. Say the word, I will be changed; where I am dry and thir-sty, send cool, re-fresh-ing rain, say the word.

Chorus

His tears have fal-len like rain

3. Say the word, I will be poor,
That I might know the riches
That You have in store.
Say the word, I will be weak;
Your strength will be the power
That satisfies the meek.
Say the word.

Chorus 2
The Lord will see the travail of His soul,
And He and I will be satisfied.
Complete the work You have started in me:
O, come Lord Jesus, shake my life again.

I will sing of the Lamb

Ps 132:9; Prov 16:18
Is 61:10; Mt 9:36-38
14:14; Mk 6:34; Lk10:2
Jn 9:39; Rom 6:9; Gal 2:20
Eph 5:2; Phil 2:8; 1 Pet 2:24; Rev 5:9

Stuart Townend

1. I will sing of the Lamb, of the
(2.) sing of His blood that

price that was paid for me, pur - chased by God, giv-ing
flows for my wret-ched-ness, wounds that are bared, that

all He could give! Here now I stand in the
I may be healed; pow'r and com - pas - sion, the

gar - ments of right-eous-ness; death has no hold, for in
marks of His mi - nis - try: may they be mine as I

3. Once I was blind, yet believed I saw everything,
   Proud in my ways, yet a fool in my part;
   Lost and alone in the company of multitudes,
   Life in my body, yet death in my heart.

   Oh, I will sing of the Lamb.
   Oh, I will sing of the Lamb.
   Oh, why should the King save a sinner like me?
   Hallelujah, hallelujah.

4. What shall I give to the Man who gave everything,
   Humbling Himself before all He had made?
   Dare I withold my own life from His sovereignty?
   I shall give all for the sake of His name!

   Oh, I will sing of the Lamb.
   Oh, I will sing of the Lamb.
   I'll sing of His love for the rest of my days!
   Hallelujah, hallelujah.

PERSONAL WORSHIP

In 1999, Kingsway approached me about doing another solo album after *Say the Word*. I had been involved in a large number of live recordings, and I felt it was time to do something different. I didn't really want to just do polished 'studio' versions of worship songs that might be pleasant to listen to but lacked the vitality of the congregation singing them as part of an act of worship.

At the same time I had begun to feel cautious about the degree of attention being given to the church 'worship time'. Most of the growing number of books, conferences and songs seemed to focus on congregational worship – the skills of leading and playing, the experience of worshipping together – but very little was being said about how we should worship in the other six days and twenty-three hours of the week!

This sense was only increased by reading the Scriptures, which seemed to focus on thanksgiving, prayer and love for God in the warp and woof of daily life rather than in weekly church services.

So I began to write more personal songs: songs that would be appropriate in my own personal devotions; songs that drew me to God when I was working or taking a walk; songs that lifted my head when I felt weighed down with the week's problems; songs that expressed the pain as well as the pleasure of life. In short, more psalm-like songs, I suppose.

Writing them was a liberating experience. Writing songs for Sunday congregational use so often focuses on such a tiny slice of real life, and results in a disconnect between what we are 'in church' and what we are the rest of the time. Here I found I could be brutally honest with my struggles and frustrations, and very specific in my sense of wonder.

I hope that these songs help others to find a fresh voice of worship in their daily lives.

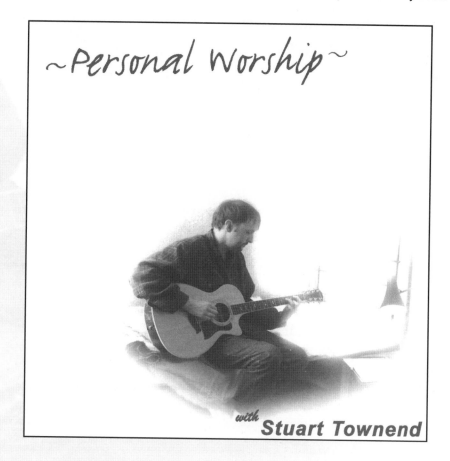

~Personal Worship~

with Stuart Townend

Like the sunshine

Ps 19:1; 46:10;
Zeph 3:17; Rom 8:6

Stuart Townend

2. Like the nurture of a baby
   At its mother's breast;
   Like the closeness of a lover,
   Like two souls at rest:
   These things I knew before,
   But never have they spoken such peace to me;
   Oh, the wonder of a Maker
   Whose heart delights in me.

3. Like the vastness of a desert,
   Like the ocean's roar;
   Like the greatness of the mountains,
   Where the eagles soar:
   These things I knew before,
   But never have they spoken such power to me;
   Oh, the wonder of a Maker
   Whose heart delights in me.

O my soul, arise and bless your Maker

Ps 86:15;
139:18; Jn 6:48;
1 Cor 13:12; 2 Cor 12:10; Rev 5:9

Stuart Townend

I will sing for all— my days— of hea-ven's love— come down. Each

breath I take will speak— His praise— un - til He calls— me

D.C. (v.3)

home.

Verse 4

Je - sus.

4. Stir in me the songs that You— are sing - ing; fill my gaze with

things as yet— un - seen.——— Give me faith to

30

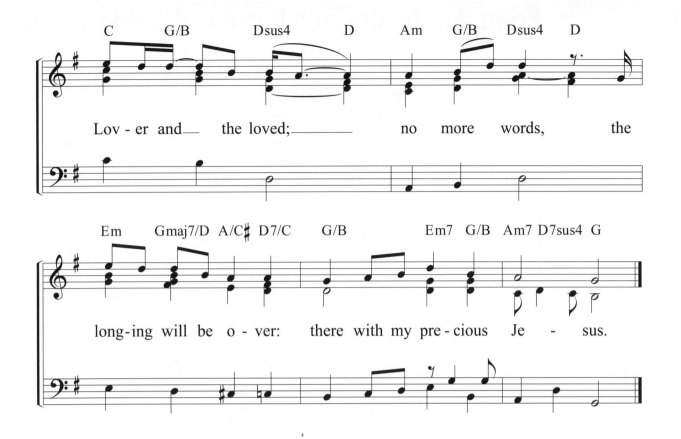

STORY BEHIND THE SONG
FROM THE SQUALOR (IMMANUEL)

This is a narrative song about Christ's birth, life, death, resurrection and impending return. People often find 'story songs' easy to understand and relate to, and this one in particular focuses on His humanity, His compassion, His empathy, His own betrayal and suffering, yet His determination to win through for the sake of the human race.

The song starts with the Christmas story – probably the most familiar of the Christian narratives in our culture. Yet its retelling often becomes so softened and sanitised (often, ironically, by the carols we sing) that its significance is greatly reduced.

In the first verse of this song I wanted to recapture some of the shocking reality of the birth of the Son of God – the scandal of an unmarried mother giving birth in a squalid, cold stable – and that God should choose for Himself such a humble path.

The final verse, about Jesus' return, is in some ways uncomfortable, but is a necessary part of our understanding of 'the end of the story', and the vital importance of receiving God's saving grace in Christ.

From the squalor of a borrowed stable

Is 42:3; 53:5;
Mt 1:18-23; 11:19;
Lk 1:34-35; 2:7-13; 4:1; 22:48 1Thess 4:16;
Heb 2:9, 14; 4:15-16; 7:25; Rev 20:15; 21:2

(Immanuel)

Stuart Townend

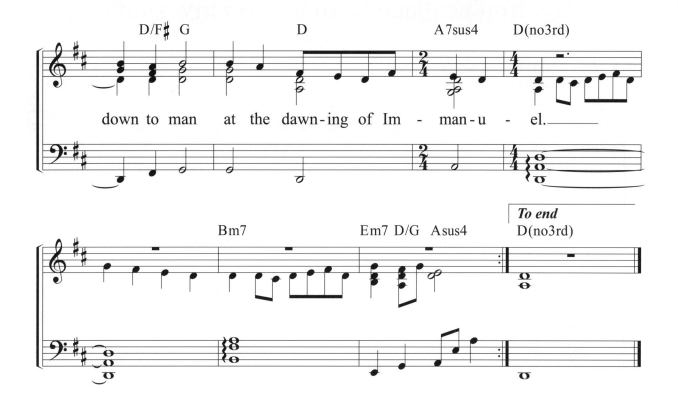

down to man   at the dawn-ing of Im - man-u - el.

2. King of heaven now the Friend of sinners,
   Humble servant in the Father's hands,
   Filled with power and the Holy Spirit,
   Filled with mercy for the broken man.
   Yes, He walked my road and He felt my pain,
   Joys and sorrows that I know so well;
   Yet His righteous steps give me hope again –
   I will follow my Immanuel!

3. Through the kisses of a friend's betrayal,
   He was lifted on a cruel cross;
   He was punished for a world's trangressions,
   He was suffering to save the lost.
   He fights for breath, He fights for me,
   Loosing sinners from the claims of hell;
   And with a shout our souls are free –
   Death defeated by Immanuel!

4. Now He's standing in the place of honour,
   Crowned with glory on the highest throne,
   Interceding for His own belovèd
   Till His Father calls to bring them home!
   Then the skies will part as the trumpet sounds
   Hope of heaven or the fear of hell;
   But the Bride will run to her Lover's arms,
   Giving glory to Immanuel!

You've placed a hunger in my heart
(Come to us)

1 Kings 19:12;
Mt 11:12; Jas 2:13; 1 Pet 2:5

Stuart Townend

1. You've placed a hun - ger in my heart to see Your glo- - ry, You've caused a thirst that I can - not ig-nore; You've stirred a pas - sion that will drive me to Your pre - sence, and I won't rest un - til You've heard me cry for more.

long as You come___ to us.___

2. Though people mock the church and curse the One who made them,
   Your kingdom is advancing every day;
   Like living stones we're being built into a temple,
   We've seen the glory and we cannot turn away.

3. Is this the summer that will see a mighty harvest?
   A sense of expectation fills the air;
   Though sin abounds, Your love is streaming to the nations,
   Let mercy triumph over judgement everywhere.

   Come to the politician, come to the refugee,
   Come to the victim of respectable society;
   Come to the mighty fallen, come to the poor oppressed:
   We don't care how You come, as long as You come to them.

I know not why God's wondrous grace

Music: Stuart Townend

3. I know not how the Spirit moves,
   Convincing men of sin;
   Revealing Jesus through the word,
   Creating faith in Him.

4. I know not what of good or ill
   May be reserved for me,
   Of weary ways or golden days
   Before His face I see.

5. I know not when my Lord may come;
   I know not how or where,
   If I shall pass the vale of death,
   Or meet Him in the air.

D.W. Whittle (1840-1901)
(adapt. Stuart Townend)

Your love
(Pour over me)

Hos 6:3; Joel 2:23;
Mt 11:28; Jn 15:11; 1 Pet 5:7

Stuart Townend

1. Your love, shin-ing like the sun, pour-ing like the rain, rag-ing like the storm, re-fresh-ing me a - gain. Ooh,_____ I re-ceive Your love._____ 2. Your

Pour o - ver me,___ pour o - ver me,___

___ let Your rain flood this thirs-ty soul.___ Pour o-ver me___

1.,3.

D.C.(v.3)/al fine

___ Your waves of love,___ pour o - ver me.___

2.

D.S.S.

___ pour o - ver me.

2. Your grace frees me from the past,
   It purges every sin,
   It purifies my heart
   And heals me from within,
   I receive Your grace.

   Pour over me

3. I come and lay my burden down
   Gladly at Your feet,
   I'm opening up my heart,
   Come make this joy complete;
   I receive Your peace.

   Pour over me x2

39

Come, see this glorious Light
(Blessing and honour)

Is 53:5; 55:1; Hag 2:7;
Jn 20:20; 1 Pet 2:24;
1 Jn 2:2; Rev 1:17; 5:11-13;
7:9; 15:3; 19:11; 22:12

Stuart Townend

glo - ry and pow'r,___ bles - sing and ho - nour and
Lamb who was slain,___ they're cry - ing 'ho - ly' a -

glo - ry and pow'r to You Lord, You're the King___
gain and a - gain, Lord Je - sus, You're the King___

1.
— of the A - ges.

2.
— of the A - ges.___

D.C.(v.2) | To end

2. Come, all you thirsty and poor,
   Come and feast on Him,
   That your souls may live
   And be satisfied.
   Come from the ends of the earth,
   Every tribe and tongue,
   Lift your voice and praise
   Your eternal Reward.
   He's the Desire of the nations,
   He is the Faithful and True.

I'm coming to the cross again
(When You touch me)

Is 53:3, 5, 7;
Mt 27:14, 29, 40;
Lk 9:51; 15:21; 23:9; 1 Cor 3:12

Stuart Townend

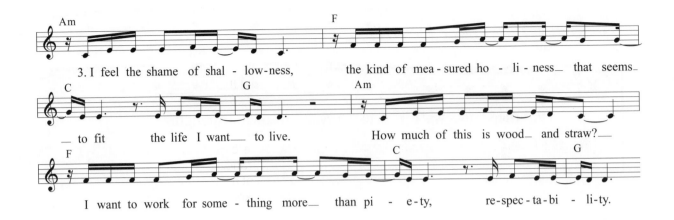

3. I feel the shame of shal - low-ness, the kind of mea - sured ho - li - ness__ that seems__ __ to fit the life I want__ to live. How much of this is wood__ and straw?__ I want to work for some - thing more__ than pi - e-ty, re - spec - ta - bi - li-ty.

4. And when the words cut like__ a knife__ and harsh re - jec - tion haunts my life,__ I tell__ __ my-self this was the pain__ You felt. You walked this road a thou - sand times, the vic - tim of the cruel - lest crimes,__ and left__ for dead__ by ev - 'ry friend__ __ You had.__ 5. And when the ac - cu - sa - tions came__ and You re-fused to play__ their game: no words__ of hate__ to set the re - cord straight. And when they taunt - ed at__ the cross 'if You are God, then save__ Your - self!'__ You set__ __ Your face__ to free this fal - len race.__

LORD OF EVERY HEART

This album came at a very busy time in my life, when I was travelling a lot as well as being heavily involved in my work with Kingsway. As a result, I concluded that the only way the recording was going to happen was if someone else 'took the reins', oversaw the whole production process, and I had as little to do with it as possible!

That person was John Hartley, and the result was one of the best sounding albums I've had the privilege to be involved with! The quality of sound, the arrangements, the playing, the mix, are all in a different league, and the development of a style that moves seamlessly between the congregational and performance is something that I have looked for ever since.

Again it has been heartening to see a number of these songs make their way into the repertoire of many local churches around the world, in particular *Grace, Across the lands* and *When love came down*.

Image of invisible God

Ps 36:9; 46:2-4; Is 9:6;
Mk 10:45; Jn 15:15; Col 1:15-17; Heb 1:6

Stuart Townend & J. K. Jamieson

♩ = 75

1. I - mage of in - vi - si - ble God,___
2. Ho - ly One whom an - gels at - tend,___

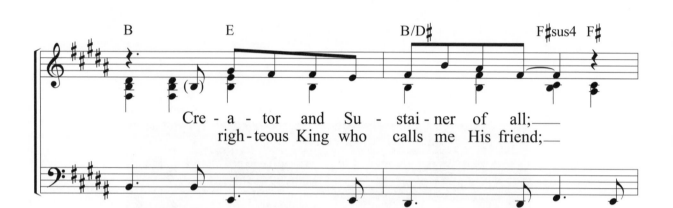

Cre - a - tor and Su - stai - ner of all;___
righ - teous King who calls me His friend;___

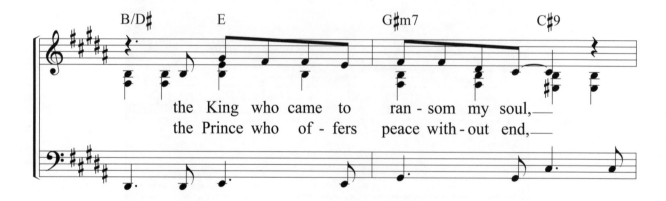

the King who came to ran - som my soul,___
the Prince who of - fers peace with - out end,___

thank You for Your per - fect love.___
thank You for Your per - fect love.___

And it's

3. Therefore I will not be afraid,
   Though mountains fall and rivers may rage;
   I'm safe within the city You've made,
   Thank You for Your perfect love.

With a prayer
(Love incarnate)

Is 53:5, 7; 58:7; Mk 1:25, 41; 8:34;
10:21; 14:22; Lk 8:24; 9:16; 23:34;
Jn 1:10, 14; 11:43; 12:32; 1 Jn 1:2; Rev 12:11

Stuart Townend

2. As a sheep before the shearer
   You were silent in Your pain;
   You endured humiliation
   At the hands of those You'd made.
   And as hell unleashed its fury
   You were lifted on a tree,
   Crying 'Father God, forgive them,
   Place their punishment on me.'

3. I will feed the poor and hungry,
   I will stand up for the truth;
   I will take my cross and follow
   To the corners of the earth.
   And I ask that You so fill me
   With Your peace, Your power, Your breath,
   That I never love my life so much
   To shrink from facing death.

What wonder of grace
(My desire)

Ps 27:4; 85:10; 100:4;
Mt 6:11; 2 Cor 12:9;
Eph 1:7-8; Phil 4:12

Stuart Townend

♩ = 79

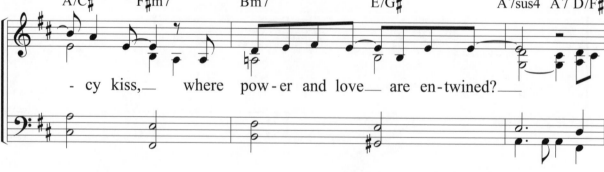

1. What won-der of grace is this, what sto-ry of pas-sion di-vine, where judge-ment and mer-cy kiss, where pow-er and love are en-twined?

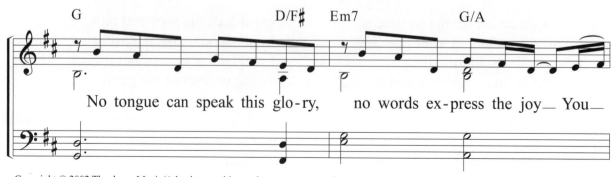

No tongue can speak this glo-ry, no words ex-press the joy You

2. Your will is my daily bread,
   Enough for my plenty and need;
   I'll live by the words You've said,
   And follow wherever You lead.
   And though my flesh may fail me,
   You prove Your grace in all I do,
   Lord, my heart is devoted to You.

Lord of every heart

Is 43:19; Jn 4:14;
Eph 5:18; Phil 3:8; Rev 4:10

Stuart Townend

1. Lord of e-v'ry heart, I'm com-ing back to You. I'm stand-ing in the shal - lows of what Your love can do; Re-mem-ber-ing the joy of laugh-ter in the rain, I'm call-ing from the de - sert, won't You fill me a-gain?

2. Lord of every deed,
   Your promise is enough;
   You're unreserved in mercy,
   And unrestrained in love.
   I'm casting down these crowns
   Of all that I can do;
   I'm trading my ambitions
   For a touch of You.

When Love came down

Is 53:5; Mt 11:19, 28;
Lk 1:52; Jn 15:11; 1 Pet 5:7

Stuart Townend

2. When every unclean thought,
   And every sinful deed
   Was scourged upon His back
   And hammered through His feet.
   The Innocent is cursed,
   The guilty are released;
   The punishment of God
   On God has brought me peace.

3. Come lay your heavy load
   Down at the Master's feet;
   Your shame will be removed,
   Your joy will be complete.
   Come crucify your pride,
   And enter as a child;
   For those who bow down low
   He'll lift up to His side.

Lord, I'm grateful

(Grace)

Ps 63:3; Is 64:6; Rom 1:17;
5:19; 2 Cor 8:9; Eph 1:5; 2:8;
1 Tim 2:6; 1 Pet 1:18-19

Stuart Townend
& Fred J Heumann

Capo 3(G)

♩ = 97

56

57

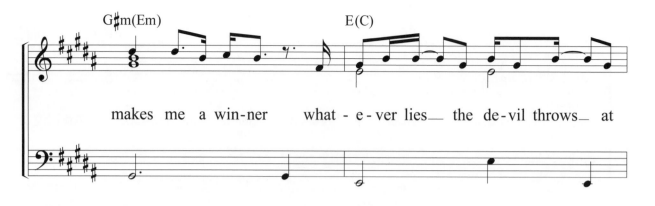

makes me a win-ner   what - e - ver lies___ the de-vil throws___ at

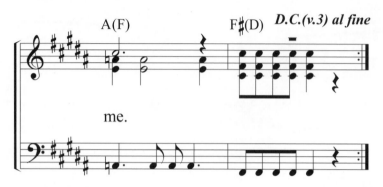

me.

2. Called and chosen when I was far away,
   You brought me into Your family.
   Free, forgiven, my guilt is washed away;
   Your loving kindness is life to me.

3. Freely given, but bought with priceless blood,
   My life was ransomed at Calvary.
   There my Jesus gave everything He could
   That I might live for eternity.

MONUMENT TO MERCY

I have been very privileged over the years to be able to work closely with a good friend of mine, who also happens to be a world-class jazz pianist, and an amazing pop arranger and producer! Mark Edwards always brings such a freshness and quality to what he does, that when the idea for the *Monument to Mercy* album came up, he was the obvious person to drive it.

Mark and I shared a concern that 'worship music' seemed to be increasingly identified with quite a narrow musical style. At a time when there were so many musical genres readily available to us, and more and more training was becoming available to the church musician, the level of creativity and innovation seemed to be going down. We found ourselves asking (only half tongue-in-cheek): Does God really only want to be worshipped to the sound of U2 and Coldplay?

So we looked a bit further afield, to musical styles where the piano was the central instrument (we are both primarily piano players, after all). Alongside a strong classical influence, the music of Ben Folds, Rufus Wainwright, Andrae Crouch, Bruce Hornsby and Billy Joel played its part in shaping an album that works from a foundation of piano, bass and drums, but pulls in gospel choirs, guitars, a string orchestra, and yes, even an air-raid siren…

Musically, it's far and away the most creative thing I've been involved with, and the most enjoyable. And Mark's arrangement of Psalm 23 still brings a lump to the throat. Our hope was that the album might help to broaden people's musical horizons to embrace a variety of God-given genres.

We've included here the full piano arrangements to many of the songs (with a separate melody line), so pianists can reproduce as closely as possible the parts on the album. As an alternative to the full piano arrangements, standard sheet music for these songs is available on the CD-ROM included with this songbook.

In every day that dawns

1 Chron 29:11; Ps 17:8; 84:11

(I'm grateful)

Stuart Townend & Kate Simmonds
Orig. piano arr. Mark Edwards

-ful for this life___ I live,___ for the mer - cies that You pour___ on me,___ and the bles - sings that meet ev - 'ry need,___ and the grace___ that is chan-ging me___ from a hope-less case___ to a child that's free.___

1. In ev - ry day that dawns I see the light of Your splen-

-dom of Your sov- 'reign plan. There are no sha-

-dows in___ Your faith - ful-ness, there are no li-

-mits to___ Your love.___ There are no sha-

-dows in___ Your faith - ful-ness, there are no li-

-mits to___ Your love.___ I'm grate-

66

67

The Lord's my Shepherd

Ps 23:1-6; 36:8; 56:3

(Psalm 23)

Stuart Townend
Orig. piano arr. Mark Edwards

Flowing

♩ = 78

Amaj9   B7sus4   C#m9

Amaj9   B7sus4   C#m9

1.The Lord's my

Amaj9   B7sus4   C#m9

Shep - herd, I'll not want;   He makes me
(2.) ways   in   righ-teous-ness,   and He a-

Amaj9   B7sus4   C#m9

lie   in   pas-tures   green.   He leads me
noints   my   head with   oil,   and my

NOTE: This arrangement can only be played fully as a duet. Alternatively, if playing with a band, the pianist should play the arpeggios and leave the bass line to the bass guitarist or another keyboard part.

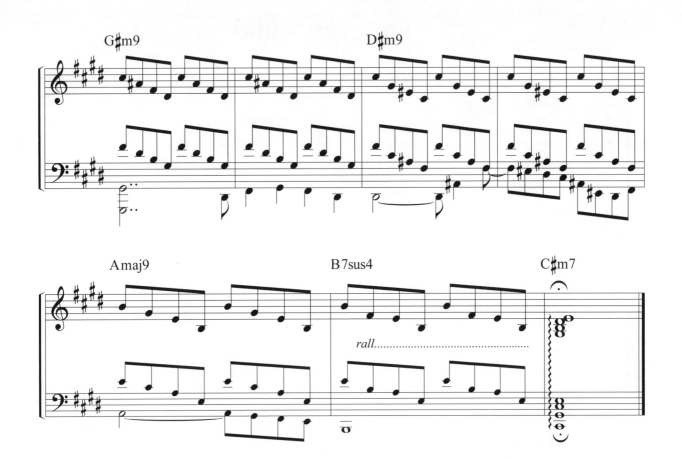

For every child
(Kyrie)

Stuart Townend

2. For every wife who cries
When her husband's lying eyes
Give the sordid game away,
And something dies within.
For those who walk the streets
Destitute and desperate;
We shake our heads and wash our hands
And hurry on our way.

day   while   na-ture chokes_ a-long_ the way._____   How

Cb(Bb)   Gb(F)   Ebm7(Dm)   Db(C) Db7sus4(C)

_   to   make a   vir-tue out_ of greed;_____   we've

ma-ny years_ be-fore_ we   pay?   Per - haps we're pay -

Gb(F)   Bbm7(Am)   Cb(Bb)   Gb/Bb(F) Abm7(Gm) Db7sus4(C)

set our hearts_ on world-ly things_____   that   can-not sa -

1.
Gb(F)   Cb/Gb(Bb)   *2.*
                                      Gb(F)

- tis-fy._   We've   - ing now?_

(Dm)   (Dm)
Chorus Abm7(Gm) Ebm/Gb Db/F(C) Gb(F)   Abm7(Gm) Ebm/Gb Bbm7(Am) Eb7(D)

Lord,   have   mer - cy,_   Christ,   have   mer - cy,_

78

Lord, have mer - cy,— have mer - cy on us all.

STORY BEHIND THE SONG
FOR EVERY CHILD (KYRIE)

This was another of those songs that sprang from rereading the Psalms, and seeing the depth of anguish and anger the psalmist directs at God for the state of the world, and God's apparent lack of intervention in it.

In this song I wanted to create a series of 'snapshot' situations that might have resonance in our own experiences and of those of the people around us. Some of them are the result of mankind's selfishness on a global or individual scale; others are just tragic or brutal circumstances in life. All of them bring suffering and sorrow to our lives, and cause us to ask the question 'Why?'

The Kyries are of course the part of the church liturgy where we say 'Lord, have mercy, Christ have mercy' and ultimately all we can do when faced with these situations is to pray for God to intervene in some way.

There may be verses that take on a particular personal significance for you in your own life, or in the lives of those around you, and I hope that the song may help you to respond with a Kyrie prayer for them.

From the breaking of the dawn

Ps 23:4; 89:28; Mt 24:35;
Jn 10:4; 16:7; Rom 3:22; 8:1-2;
2 Cor 12:9; Phil 1:6; Heb 8:12; 1 Jn 4:18

(Every promise)

Stuart Townend & Keith Getty

1. From the break - ing of the dawn to the set - ting of the sun, I will stand on ev-'ry pro-mise of Your word.

stum - ble and I sin, con - dem - na - tion pres - sing in, I will stand on ev-'ry pro-mise of Your word.

faced with an - guished choice, I will lis - ten for Your voice, and I'll stand on ev-'ry pro-mise of Your word.

lifts me from des - pair, love that casts out ev - 'ry fear, as I stand on ev-'ry pro-mise of Your word.

81

this I am se - cure, I can stand on ev-'ry pro-mise of Your
mem - ber sins no more! So I'll stand on ev-'ry pro-mise of Your
work be - gun in me, so I'll stand on ev-'ry pro-mise of Your
all who will be - lieve; we will stand on ev-'ry pro-mise of Your

Last time to Coda ⊕

1.,2.

word.
word.
word.
word.

2. When I
3. When I'm

3. **Slowly** *accel.*

4. Hope that

A tempo

D.S.

What love has captured me?

(Filled with wonder)

Eph 3:19

Ian & Stuart Townend
Orig. piano arr. Mark Edwards

With energy

♩ = 135

Doo doo doo doo doo____ doo doo doo doo doo____

1. What love has cap-tured me,____ what mer-cy filled____ my soul,____

that calls the sin - ner clean,___ and makes the woun - ded whole.___ Too high___ for words___ to tell,___ for minds___ to com - pre - hend.___ 'Cause I'm

filled with___ the life___ of God,___ thrilled with___ the Fa -
Grate - ful___ that I___ should be___ part of___ Your fa -

Last time to Coda ⊕   C   G/C

- ther's love,— and as I } wor-ship— my heart— is filled— with won-
- mi - ly,— and as I }

Dm7/C   1.
                                         F

- der.   2.When hope a-

G   C/E   F

ban-dons me,— I call to mind— what's true:—   my faith is

G   C/E   F

not in me,— but what my God— can do.—

86

His words— have pow'r— to turn— the night— to glo - rious day.

D.S. 2.

— 'Cause I'm

(Ooohs - on repeat only)

(trumpet)

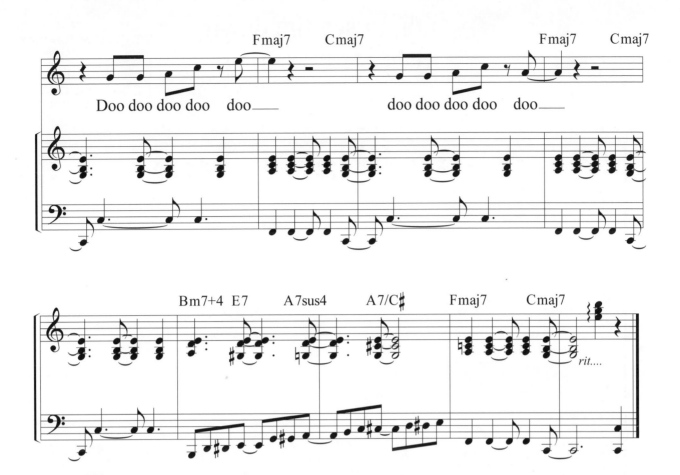

Doo doo doo doo   doo____   doo doo doo doo   doo____

Oh, to see the dawn

Is 53:5, 11-12; Mt 27:45, 51-52;
Lk 24:7; Jn 19:30;
2 Cor 5:21; Col 1:18

(The power of the cross)

Keith Getty & Stuart Townend
Orig. piano arr. Mark Edwards

With feeling

♩ = 124

1. Oh, to see the dawn of the dark - est
2. Oh, to see the pain writ - ten on Your

day: Christ on the road to Cal - va -
face bear - ing the awe - some weight of

sin for us, took the blame,

bore the wrath: we stand for-giv-en at the

cross.

3. Now the day-light flees, now the ground be-

wounds, for through Your suff-'ring I am free. Death is crushed to death, life is mine to live, won through Your self-less love. This, the power

STORY BEHIND THE SONG
OH, TO SEE THE DAWN (THE POWER OF THE CROSS)

This song attempts to tell a story, to paint the scene of Christ's death on the cross. I've tried to include the little pictorial details and show their significance in the overall picture.

Sometimes Bible stories are so familiar, we fail to be shocked or moved by them, and the crucifixion is no exception. Movies like *The Passion of the Christ* can help bring the story to life again. But songs can do this as well, perhaps in an even more profound and enduring way. Unlike film, they paint the picture on the most powerful canvas – our imaginations – with the combination of poetic lyric and crafted melody, in a way that can move and inspire us again and again.

This song actually took a long time to finish. Perhaps surprisingly it wasn't the verses that I got stuck on, but the chorus. I must have written at least a dozen different possibilities which I sent to Keith, and which – quite rightly – got a lukewarm response. We finally narrowed it down to two ideas, and couldn't make the final decision – so just used them both! That's why there is a chorus to use between the verses and a final chorus to end the song.

Blessèd Spirit of the King

(Puritan Prayer)

2 Cor 7:10; 12:10

Stuart Townend

1. Bles-sèd Spi-rit of— the King, of grace and love the Au -
thor, work re-pent-ance deep— with - in, and bend me at Your
al - tar. Melt my heart with ma-je-sty, then
show my ru-ined self to me; teach me to more clear - ly
see Your might and will to save me.

2. Here I place without reserve
   My soul in faith and meekness,
   Trusting in Christ's power and love
   To flourish in my weakness.
   Cause my days on earth to be
   Through time and through eternity
   A trophy of His victory,
   A monument to mercy.

3. Teach me to behold my God,
   And trust His power to save me,
   Arms outstretched in constant love,
   Whose strength will never fail me.
   Help me to commune with Him,
   Depend and follow after Him,
   That through my life His peace will reign,
   And joy be my companion.

Belovèd and Blessèd

Ps 23:1; 103:8; Song 2:16; 6:3;
Mal 4:2; Mt 3:17; 17:5;
Jn 4:14; 6:33; 15:15; 1 Cor 1:30;
2 Cor 1:3; Eph 1:6; 1 Tim 2:6;
Heb 10:22; 13:8; Jas 4:8; 1 Jn 1:1; 4:18; Rev 5:5-6

Gently

Stuart Townend
Orig. piano arr. Mark Edwards

1. Be - lov - èd___ and
(2.&3.) Bro - ther,___ my
(4.) kind - ness, com -

Bles - sèd,___ the Fa - ther's pure___ de - light.___
Com - for - ter,___ my Shep - herd and___ my Friend.___
pas - sion___ for those who will___ draw near;___

Re - dee - mer,___ Su -
My Ran - som,___ my
ac - cep - tance,___ for -

101

Bbm Eb7/G Ab Db7sus4 Db7
Breath of life, Sun of right - eous-ness, You're the
be - ing cries, 'Lord be glo - ri - fied by
Gb
1.
Ab Ebm7 Gbmaj9 Ab Dbsus4 Db
Love that sa - tis-fies.
ev - 'ry-thing I am.'
Ab7sus4/Db Ab7/Db Ebm/Db Db
D.S.(v.3)
3. My
2.
Ab
D.S.S.
3.
Ab Ebm7 Gbmaj9 Ab
You're the

103

Knowing Your grace
(Child of the King)

Ps 17:8; 63:7; Is 6:7;
Song 1:4; Mt 11:28; Jn 14:27;
Gal5:1; Eph 1:4-5, 8; Phil 1:6; 1 Jn 3:1

Stuart Townend & Terry Virgo
Orig. piano arr. Mark Edwards

Brightly

♩ = 87

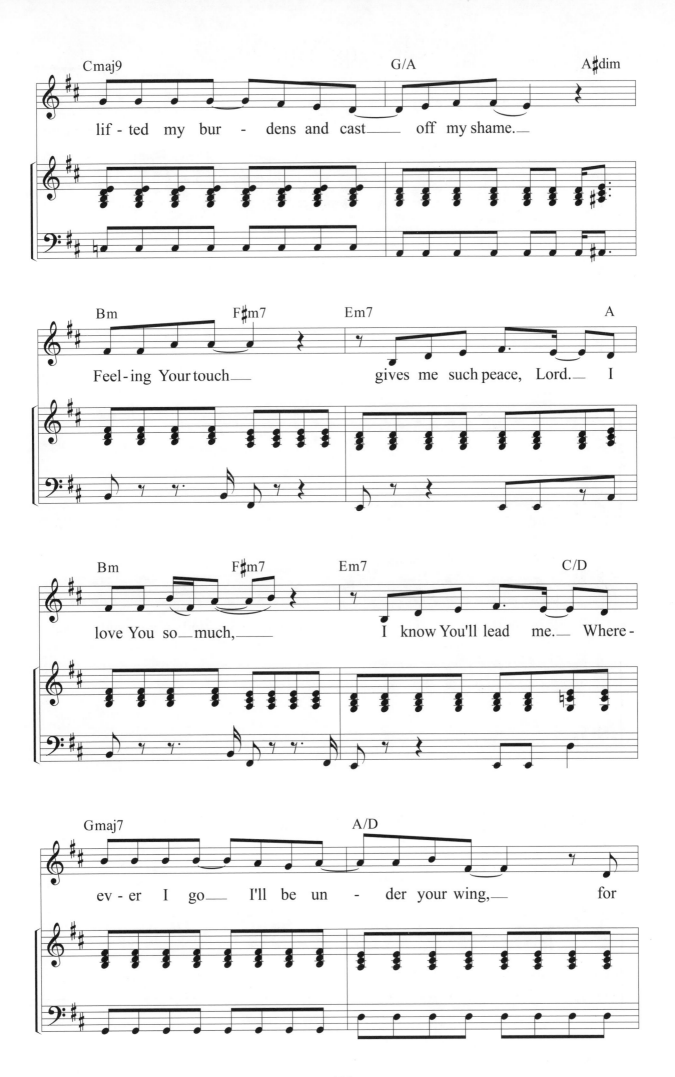

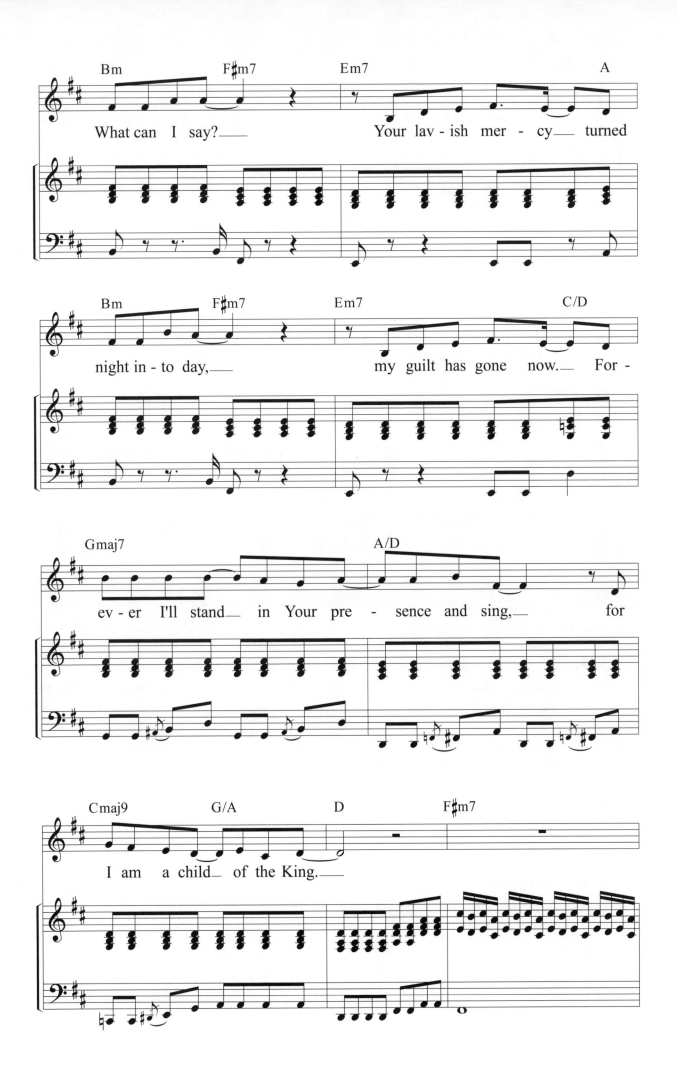

109

Bm F♯m7 Em7 F♯m7 Bm F♯m7
Know-ing Your grace
Em7 A Bm F♯m7
has set me free, Lord. I'm seek-ing Your face,
Em7 C/D Gmaj7
I feel Your plea - sure, Your joy in the ones You have cho -
A/D Cmaj9
- sen by name. You've lif - ted my bur - dens and cast
G/A A♯dim Bm F♯m7
off my shame. Feel-ing Your touch

STORY BEHIND THE SONG
MY GOD

My God was one of those songs that popped up from nowhere… I never meant to write a gospel song, but it came to me as I was playing the piano one day, and reflecting on the glorious, radical life of Christ, and His ability in every situation to make broken people whole – physically, mentally, emotionally and spiritually. And it's something He is still doing today for those who are prepared to admit they are broken.

It's not necessarily a congregational song, although I have often done it very successfully with a choir singing the backing vocals! And I've found it very useful as an evangelistic song, encouraging people to think about their lives, and what may be stopping them from giving their lives wholeheartedly to Him.

My God

- ding, yet cry-ing 'Fa - ther God,— for-give.' My God—

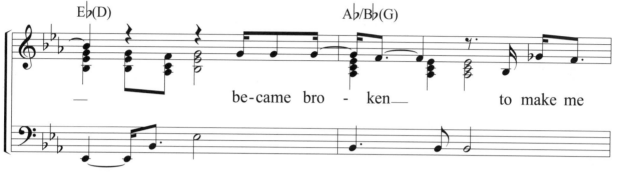

— be-came bro - ken— to make me

whole._____ 6. My_____

2. My God touched the outcast,
Raised the lame man,
And He caused the blind to see.
My God takes the broken
And makes them whole.

3. My God stood for justice,
Shamed the prideful,
But He called the sinner 'friend'.
My God takes the broken
And makes them whole.

4. My God felt the anguish
Of the soldier,
Made his child to live again.
My God takes the broken
And makes them whole.

5. My God, mocked and beaten,
Crushed and bleeding,
Yet crying 'Father God, forgive.'
My God became broken
To make me whole.

6. My God, on the third day,
In the morning
Broke the shackles of the grave.
My God takes the broken
And makes them whole.

7. My God knows my failures,
Speaks forgiveness,
Gives me strength to try again.
My God takes the broken
And makes me whole.

See what a morning

Dan 7:13-14; Mt 28:3,6;
Jn 20:7, 11-12, 16; Rom 6:5
Eph 2:6; 2 Tim 2:12; Rev 11:15; 20:6

(Resurrection hymn)

Keith Getty & Stuart Townend
Orig. piano arr. Mark Edwards

Ooh

1. See,____ what a morn - ing, glo - rious - ly bright, with the
2. See____ Ma - ry weep - ing: 'where____ is He laid?' as in

dawn - ing of hope in Je - ru - sa - lem;
sor - row she turns from the emp - ty tomb;

116

con - quered;   and   we   will

reign   with   Him,   for   He   lives,   Christ   is   ri-sen   from   the

dead!

Ooh

(2nd time fine)

THERE IS A HOPE

In 2007 I felt it was time to record some new songs, in the context in which they were meant to be used – with the congregation. As a result, we pulled together a great band and spent several days arranging and rehearsing, before going out to Northern Ireland to record a live album and DVD in Coleraine. So it was particularly appropriate that the album has a strong folk feel, with fiddle, piano accordion and uillean pipes.

Since an early age I have been very drawn to folk music originating from the four corners of the British Isles. I have been struck by its purity of sound, its accessible melodies, its story-telling tradition, its use of acoustic instruments, and its appropriateness in small community settings rather than large stadium-type arenas – all of which makes it particularly suited to the local church setting.

I'm very pleased with the songs, especially with the title track (co-written with Mark Edwards), which already seems to be of help to many who are going through difficult times. The context for pieces such as *Communion Hymn* and *Benediction* should be self-explanatory!

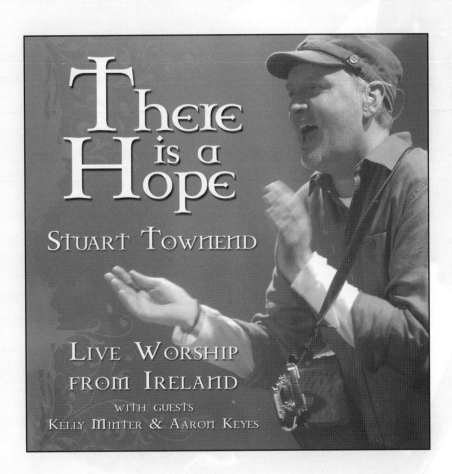

You're the Word of God the Father

(Across the lands)

Ps 96:11; Lk 8:24;
9:16; 19:10; Jn 1:1, 3; Eph 4:8;
Col 1:16-17; Heb 7:25; Rev 7:9

Stuart Townend & Keith Getty

1. You're the Word of God the Fa-ther,_ from be-fore the world be-gan;_ e-v'ry star and e-v'ry
2. Yet You left the gaze of an-gels,_ came to seek and save the lost,_ and ex-changed the joy of

123

3. With a shout You rose vic-

tor-ious,___ wrest-ing vic-t'ry from the grave,___ and a-scend-ed in-to

hea-ven___ lead-ing cap-tives in Your wake. Now You

stand be-fore the Fa-ther__ in-ter-ced-ing for Your own.__ From each

tribe and tongue and na-tion__ You are lead-ing sin-ners

home.__ You're the Au-thor of cre-a-tion,__ You're the Lord of e-v'ry

man;__ and Your cry of love rings out a-cross the lands.__

You're the __

Let the earth resound

Gen 1:16; Ps 96:11; 146:7;
Lam 3:22; Rom 5:19; 1 Cor 13:12;
2 Cor 4:6; Eph 3:15; 4:13; 1 Tim 1:17;
Heb 5:8; 1 Jn 3:2; Rev 21:4

Keith Getty & Stuart Townend

1. Let the earth re-sound with songs of praise to the Fa-ther's power and love. For the One who set each star in place chose to set His heart on us. To the One whose might gives vic-to-ry, yet whose mer-cies ne-ver cease, as the tap-es-try of

2. Let the earth be stilled before the sight
   Of a Father's sacrifice,
   That revealed the depths of love divine
   In the face of Jesus Christ.
   Through a life of full obedience,
   And a death in agony,
   He removed the rebel's punishment
   And He set the prisoner free.

3. Let the earth resound with songs of faith
   At the wonder yet to come,
   When all sin and pain are put to death
   And the church and Christ are one.
   When we stand as God's great family
   And we meet the Father's gaze
   And we share in His eternal joy
   As we join in ceaseless praise.

Hear the call of the kingdom

Ps 103:13; Mic 6:8;
Rom 8:25; 10:14;
2 Cor 4:6; 5:19; Eph 2:4; 5:2;
Phil 2:5; Col 1:20; Heb 1:9; Rev 15:4

Capo 3 (D)

Keith & Kristyn Getty and Stuart Townend

♩ = 85

1. Hear the call of the king-dom, lift your eyes to the King,— let His song rise with-in you as a fra-grant of-fer-ing, of how God, rich in mer-cy, came in Christ to re-deem— all who trust in His un-fail-ing— grace.

2. Hear the

129

2. Hear the call of the kingdom to be children of light,
   With the mercy of heaven, the humility of Christ.
   Walking justly before Him, loving all that is right,
   That the life of Christ may shine through Him.

3. Hear the call of the kingdom to reach out to the lost,
   With the Father's compassion in the wonder of the cross,
   Bringing peace and forgiveness, and a hope yet to come;
   Let the nations put their trust in Him.

Loved before the dawn of time
(Salvation's song)

Ps 150:6;
Is 40:4-8; 53:11;
2 Cor 5:21; Eph 1:4;
Col 3:3; Rev 5:11

Stuart Townend & Andrew Small

133

Hal - le - lu - jah, I will sing with ev-'ry breath that I am gi - ven, I will

D.S.

2. When I'm stained with guilt and sin,
   He is there to lift me,
   Heal me and forgive me;
   Gives me strength to stand again,
   Stronger than I was before.

3. All the claims of Satan's curse
   Lifted through His offering,
   Satisfied through suffering;
   All the blessings He deserves
   Poured on my unworthy soul.

4. Stars will fade and mountains fall;
   Christ will shine forever,
   Love's unfading splendour.
   Earth and heaven will bow in awe,
   Joining in salvation's song.

Optional piano intro & verse 1 accompaniment

1. Loved be-fore the dawn of time, cho-sen by my Ma - ker, hid-den in my Sa - viour: I am His and He is mine, che-rished for e - ter - ni - ty.

STORY BEHIND THE SONG
THERE IS A HOPE

I particularly enjoyed writing this song, as the melody really was a collaborative process. Usually I find with co-writes that someone comes with a melody idea that is almost complete, and it just needs a tweak here and there to be finished. In this case, Mark came with a number of fantastic melodic lines, but they didn't quite seem to flow together. So I found myself inserting little melodic ideas that linked them, and as we each sat in turn at the piano, the song acquired a flow and a shape that worked really well.

We also set ourselves a challenge: to make every musical phrase different from the others. It occurs in a handful of well-known hymns (*Dear Lord and Father of mankind, Jerusalem*), but not many and it certainly is very different from the kind of hymns Keith and I write. It also makes it a bit harder for congregations to learn! But I hope it is worth the effort...

Lyrically, I had wanted to write a song about hope for a long time, as I felt it was a much misunderstood aspect of the Christian life. Hope plays a huge part in all of our lives, but the sad fact is that many of the things we put our hope in, even as Christians, are insubstantial and uncertain – a better job, recovery from illness, success for our children, and so on. But none of them come with any guarantees.

Christian hope is different. It deals with things we haven't received yet, but we can be absolutely certain we will get them! The hope that no matter how dark and difficult life gets, Christ will always be there with us; the hope that one day we will see Him face to face. These are future certainties that lift our heads and give us real hope and confidence in life.

There is a hope

Deut 33:27; Rom 8:18;
1 Cor 13:12-13; 2 Cor 1:21;
Col 1:27; 1 Pet 1:8

Stuart Townend & Mark Edwards

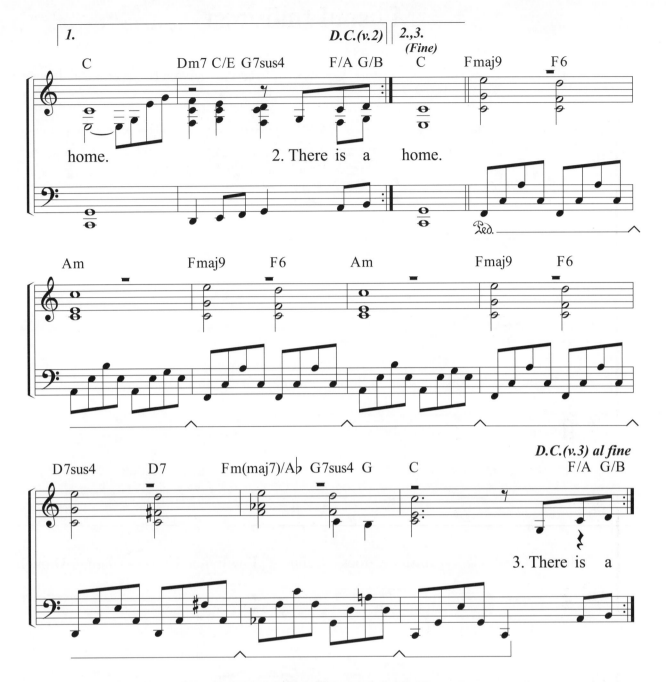

2. There is a hope that lifts my weary head,
   A consolation strong against despair,
   That when the world has plunged me in its deepest pit,
   I find the Saviour there!
   Through present sufferings, future's fear,
   He whispers 'courage' in my ear.
   For I am safe in everlasting arms,
   And they will lead me home.

3. There is a hope that stands the test of time,
   That lifts my eyes beyond the beckoning grave,
   To see the matchless beauty of a day divine
   When I behold His face!
   When sufferings cease and sorrows die,
   And every longing satisfied.
   Then joy unspeakable will flood my soul,
   For I am truly home.

My soul finds rest

Ps 62:1-2, 4-8, 10, 12; Gal 3:13

(Psalm 62)

Aaron Keyes & Stuart Townend

2. Find rest my soul in God alone
   Amid the world's temptations;
   When evil seeks to take a hold
   I'll cling to my salvation.
   Though riches come and riches go,
   Don't set your heart upon them;
   The fields of hope in which I sow
   Are harvested in heaven.

3. I'll set my gaze on God alone
   And trust in Him completely;
   With every day pour out my soul
   And He will prove His mercy.
   Though life is but a fleeting breath,
   A sigh too brief to measure,
   My King has crushed the curse of death
   And I am His forever.

My soul will sing

Ps 77:11; 103:5, 10-15, 17, 20; 138:1

(Psalm 103)

Kristyn Getty & Stuart Townend

High as the hea-vens reach a - bove the earth   is Your un -
fail - ing love,   is Your un - fail-ing love.
Far as the east is ban-ished from the west   You took our
sins from us,   re-moved our sins from us.   (How) wide,   how

3rd time D.S. al Coda
Last time to Coda

2nd time only

high,   how wide,   how high,   how wide,   how

141

2. Our King delights to show compassion to the weak;
   Their deepest needs He loves to satisfy.
   Throughout the earth his justice and His mercy speak,
   And He will run to meet the victim's cry.
   From everlasting
   To everlasting
   Our youth renewed with every step we take.

3. Though we are dust, a moment in eternity,
   As flowers bloom today and then are gone,
   He crowns our lives with beauty and with dignity;
   His patience smiles on all who turn to Him.
   From generation
   To generation
   We'll tell the story of His faithfulness!

Will You hide me in Your shelter?

(Healing streams)

Ps 30:5, 91:1;
Jn 14:16; 20:27

John Hartley, Stuart Townend
& Kelly Minter

shine Your light of faith-ful-ness, giv-ing cour-age to my soul,

1. | **D.C. (v.3)** | **2.** *Mid section*

cour-age to my—— soul? 3. Will You And

in the place where trou-ble waits, Lord, I shall not fear: the

D.C. (v.1) al fine

Com-for-ter, the Coun-sel-lor, the Sa-viour is here.—— 1. Will You

2. Will You lift my heavy burdens?
Will You pave my path with peace?
When the road is steep and stony,
Let me bathe in healing streams,
Bathe in healing streams.

3. Will You lead me to repentance?
Will you make temptations flee?
When I'm filled with condemnation,
Will You show Your scars to me,
Show Your scars to me?

To You we bring our hymn of praise

(Glory be to God)

Gen 1:3; 1 Cor 15:55; Rev 4:8; 5:9, 13

Stuart Townend, Matt Maher & Kelly Minter

= 66
Verse
D A/C♯ Bm7 G
1. To You we bring our hymn of praise;
spoke be - fore the dawn of time;
Bm D A D A/C♯ Bm7 G
glo-ry be to God. Hearts and hands to - ge - ther raised;
glo-ry be to God. Veil of dark - ness torn by light;
Bm7 A
1.,3. D.C. (v.2/4) D
2.,4.,5. D
Bridge
glo-ry_ be to God. 2. Who God. (1.,3.) And with un -
glo-ry_ be to (2.) And all Your
G Bm7 A/C♯ D G A Bm
ceas - ing voice, all hea - ven sings: glo-ry be to God; the
child - ren cry with loud ac - claim: glo-ry be to God.
G D A/C♯ Bm G A
an - them of the Lord's re - deemed: glo-ry_ be to
Sing, O church, your sweet re - frain: glo-ry_ be to

3. You purchased captives for Your saints; glory be to God.
   And opened wide the kingdom gates; glory be to God.

4. You overcame the sting of death; glory be to God.
   And clothed us in Christ's righteousness; glory be to God.

5. Father, Spirit, risen Son; glory be to God.
   Who was and is and is to come; glory be to God.

Spirit of heaven
(Christ in me)

Rom 3:22; Gal 4:19;
Phil 3:9-10; Col 1:27

Keith Getty & Stuart Townend

2. Spirit of beauty and holiness,
   Come refine with fire from above,
   Till I am cast in Your righteousness,
   And I love the things that You love.

3. Breathe Your forgiveness when darkness falls
   And my heart is heavy with sin;
   Fill me with faith for the higher cause
   Of the ceaseless praise of the king.

Behold the Lamb

(The communion hymn)

Mt 26:26-28; Lk 22:30;
Jn 1:29; 6:35, 48; Rom 8:17;
1 Cor 11:24-26; 12:27;
Eph 4:3; 1 Pet 2:24; 1 Jn 1:7

Keith and Kristyn Getty
& Stuart Townend

sign   of our bonds   of   peace   a-round the ta-ble of the

King.   King.

2. The body of our Saviour, Jesus Christ,
   Torn for you: eat and remember
   The wounds that heal, the death that brings us life,
   Paid the price to make us one.
   So we share in this Bread of Life,
   And we drink of His sacrifice,
   As a sign of our bonds of love
   Around the table of the King.

3. The blood that cleanses every stain of sin,
   Shed for you: drink and remember
   He drained death's cup that all may enter in
   To receive the life of God.
   So we share in this Bread of Life,
   And we drink of His sacrifice,
   As a sign of our bonds of grace
   Around the table of the King.

4. And so with thankfulness and faith we rise
   To respond and to remember
   Our call to follow in the steps of Christ
   As His body here on earth.
   As we share in His suffering,
   We proclaim: Christ will come again!
   And we'll join in the feast of heaven
   Around the table of the King.

STORY BEHIND THE SONG
IN CHRIST ALONE

In November 2000 I was at a worship conference in Eastbourne, and was introduced through a mutual friend to Keith Getty, who I had heard was a terrific melody-writer. We met up for a coffee, and he promised to send me a CD of song ideas.

I didn't really think any more about it. Then a CD arrived in the post containing three song ideas played on a piano. I didn't get past the first melody, because I was so taken with it – it was quite hymn-like, but with a beautiful celtic lilt. I immediately started writing down some lines on the life of Christ.

Often lyrics come in quite a haphazard way. You write loads of couplets, then rewrite some, then gradually piece them together to give continuity and shape. The process for *In Christ alone* was much more linear. Once I'd worked out the rhyming structure (it felt as though the song had better shape if lines one and three rhymed as well as the more usual two and four), I started working on the first verse, setting the scene with a fairly subjective exploration of what Christ means to the Christian. Then, as I worked through the life, death and resurrection of Christ, I was getting more and more excited and emotional, and verse four kind of spilled out as a declaration of the impact of these amazing events in our lives.

Within a couple of days I had the whole lyric and sent it to Keith. He suggested a couple of changes, and *In Christ alone* was finished.

I think maybe one of the reasons the song is so popular is that it can stir up our emotions (I still often cry like an old softie when I sing it), but the emotion is not the central feature of the song. Because the lyrics stay fixed on the unchanging truths of our salvation, it not only provokes emotion, but engenders faith, strengthening our spirits and not just stirring our souls.

In Christ alone

Capo 1 (D)

Is 53:5; Mt 27:42; Jn 1:5, 9; 10:28; 15:26;
Acts 2:32-33; Rom 5:9; 8:1-2, 38-39; 1 Cor 15:28;
Eph 2:20; 3:18; Phil 2:7-8; Col 1:27

Stuart Townend & Keith Getty

1. In Christ a-lone my hope is found, He is my light, my strength, my song; this Cor-ner-stone, this so-lid Ground, firm through the fier-cest drought and storm. What heights of love, what depths of

154

peace, when fears are stilled, when striv-ings cease! My Com-for-

ter, my All in All, here in the love of Christ I stand.

2. In Christ a - live. Christ.

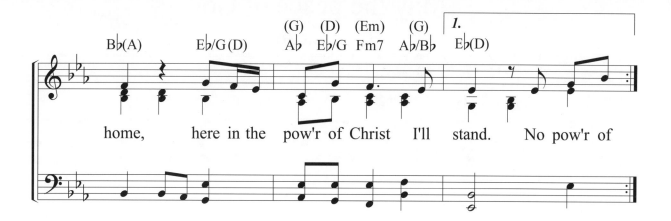

home,   here in the   pow'r of Christ   I'll   stand.   No pow'r of

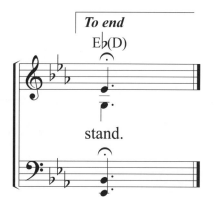

To end

stand.

2. In Christ alone! – who took on flesh,
   Fulness of God in helpless babe!
   This gift of love and righteousness,
   Scorned by the ones He came to save:
   Till on that cross as Jesus died,
   The wrath of God was satisfied –
   For every sin on Him was laid;
   Here in the death of Christ I live.

3. There in the ground His body lay,
   Light of the world by darkness slain:
   Then bursting forth in glorious Day
   Up from the grave He rose again!
   And as He stands in victory
   Sin's curse has lost its grip on me,
   For I am His and He is mine –
   Bought with the precious blood of Christ.

May the peace of God

(Benediction)

2 Cor 13:14; Phil 4:7;
Rev 17:14; 19:16

Stuart Townend & Keith Getty

2. May this peace which passes understanding,
And this grace which makes us what we are,
And this fellowship of His communion
Make us one in spirit and in heart.

Chorus x2

159

CREATION SINGS

Following on from the experience of recording the *There is a Hope* album, with *Creation Sings* I wanted to explore the folk genre more deeply, drawing on English and Scottish as well as Irish traditions, and this time working in a studio situation, where the arrangements could be more crafted and finely tuned.

I'm delighted with the result. It was great to include whistles, banjo, bouzouki, string quartet and harmonium in the sound – and there was hardly an electric guitar in sight! In particular there's a lightness and joy in reels that you find in pubs and Ceilidh clubs, but is sadly lacking in our churches. And yet whenever we have done any of the reels live in church, it never fails to bring a smile to people's lips and some movement (however slight) to their toes!

Come, people of the risen King

Ps 23:6; 30:5; 123:1;
Lam 3:22; Rom 5:2, 5;
Eph 1:7; Phil 4:4; Col 1:17;
Heb 12:4; 2 Pet 1:19; Rev 22:16

Keith & Kristyn Getty and Stuart Townend

2. Come, those whose joy is morning sun
   And those weeping through the night.
   Come, those who tell of battles won,
   And those struggling in the fight.
   For His perfect love will never change,
   And His mercies never cease,
   But follow us through all our days
   With the certain hope of peace.

3. Come, young and old from every land,
   Men and women of the faith.
   Come, those with full or empty hands,
   Find the riches of His grace.
   Over all the world His people sing,
   Shore to shore we hear them call
   The truth that cries through every age;
   Our God is all in all.

Creation sings the Father's song

Mk 13:7-8;
Rom 8:19,22;
1 Cor 15:22, 45;
2 Cor 5:19; Gal 3:13; Rev 21:1

Capo 3(G)

Keith & Kristyn Getty and Stuart Townend

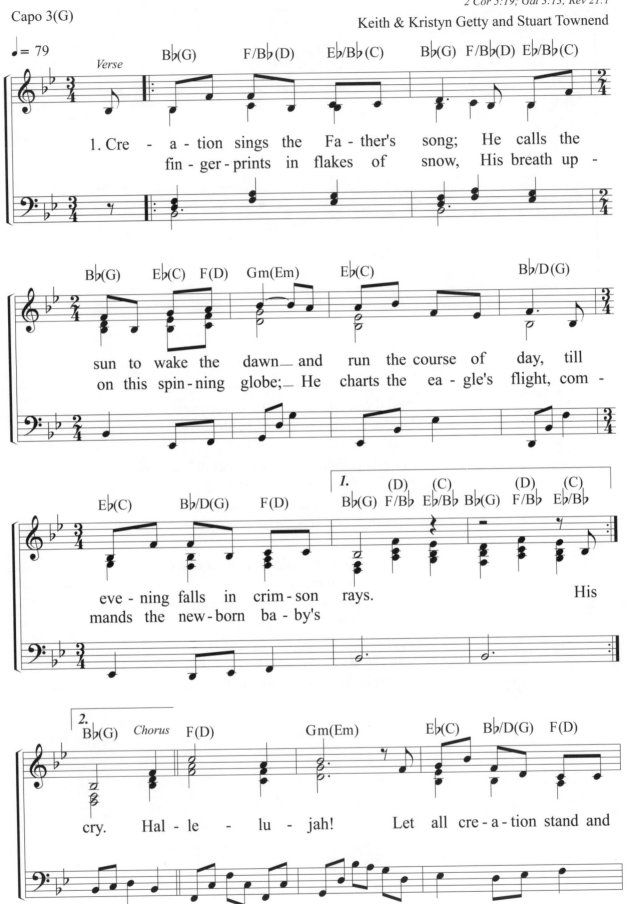

1. Cre - a - tion sings the Fa - ther's song; He calls the
fin - ger - prints in flakes of snow, His breath up -

sun to wake the dawn__ and run the course of day, till
on this spin - ning globe;__ He charts the ea - gle's flight, com -

eve - ning falls in crim - son rays. His
mands the new - born ba - by's

cry. Hal - le - lu - jah! Let all cre - a - tion stand and

sing: 'Hal - le - lu - jah!' Fill the earth with songs of

wor - ship, tell the won-ders of cre - a - tion's King.

2. Cre -
3. Cre -

2. Creation gazed upon His face;
   The Ageless One in time's embrace,
   Unveiled the Father's plan
   Of reconciling God and man.
   A second Adam walked the earth,
   Whose blameless life would break the curse,
   Whose death would set us free
   To live with Him eternally.

3. Creation longs for His return,
   When Christ shall reign upon the earth;
   The bitter wars that rage
   Are birth pains of a coming age.
   When He renews the land and sky,
   All heaven will sing and earth reply
   With one resplendent theme:
   The glory of our God and King!

You are my anchor

(The Father's embrace)

Ps 27:1-6, 11-14

Stuart Townend

2. Teach me Your way, Lord,
   Make straight the path before me.
   Do not forsake me,
   My hope is in You.
   As I walk through life, I am confident
   I will see Your goodness with every step,
   And my heart directs me to seek You in all that I do,
   So I will wait for You.

All my days
(Beautiful Saviour)

Is 9:6; Ps 18:6; 36:8-9; Jn 14:6;
1 Cor 15:54; Heb 10:22;
Rev 5:12; 11:15; 22:16

Capo 3 (D)

Stuart Townend

♩. = 58

1. All_____ my days I will sing this song of glad - ness,
2. I_____ will trust in the cross of my Re - dee - mer,

give_____ my praise to the Foun - tain of de - lights; for
I_____ will sing of the blood that ne - ver fails; of

in my help - less - ness You heard my_____ cry, and
sins for - giv - en, of con - science_____ cleansed, of

waves of mer - cy poured_ down on my life._____
death de - fea - ted and_ life with - out

172

3. I long to be where the praise is never-ending,
   Yearn to dwell where the glory never fades;
   Where countless worshippers will share one song,
   And cries of 'worthy' will honour the Lamb!

O for a closer walk with God

Ex 20:4-5; Jn 14:27; Rev 2:4

Capo 1(D)

Music: Keith Getty and Stuart Townend

1. O_ for a clos-er walk with God,_ a calm and heav'n-ly frame, a_ light to shine up-on the road_ lead-ing to the Lamb.

2. Where_ O Fire of God, come_ burn in me; re - new a ho - ly pas - sion, till Christ my deep-est_ long-ing be, my_

ne - ver fail - ing foun - tain, my— ne - ver fail - ing foun - tain. 3. What— tain. O tain, my— ne - ver fail - ing foun - tain.

2. Where is that blessédness I knew
   When first I saw the Lord?
   Where is that soul refreshing view
   Of Jesus and His word?

3. What peaceful hours I once enjoyed,
   How sweet the memory still!
   But they have left an aching void
   The world can never fill!

4. The dearest idol I have known,
   Whate'er that idol be,
   Help me to tear it from Thy throne,
   And worship only Thee.

5. So shall my walk be close with God,
   Calm and serene my frame;
   So purer light shall mark the road
   That leads me to the Lamb.

Chorus: Keith Getty and Stuart Townend
Verses: William Cowper (1731-1800)

The Light of the World

Mt 5:14; Lk 19:10;
Jn 1:3, 14; 8:12; 13:14-15;
Phil 2:8

Stuart Townend & J K Jamieson

1. The Light of the World made his-t'ry be-gin,— spoke time in-to be-ing, caused pla-nets to spin; flung ga-lax-ies wide through in-fi-nite space to sing of His splen-dour and fa-thom-less grace.

2. The felt our in-jus-tice and shared in our strife.

Chorus

Come, come, daugh-ters and sons, look to the Light of the

World. Sing, sing prais-es to Him. Sim-ply be-lieve,

Last time to Coda

you will re-ceive mer-cy and love with-out mea-

sure. 3. The

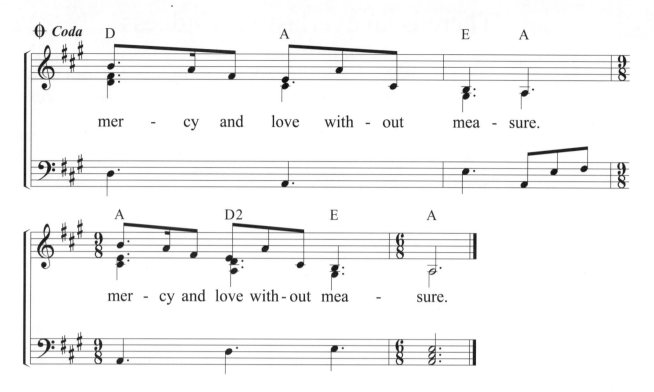

2. The Light of the World
   Now shone as a man,
   And walked through the valleys
   He'd carved with His hands.
   A servant to those
   He'd breathed into life,
   He felt our injustice
   And shared in our strife.

3. The Light of the World
   Preached justice for all,
   Defying the proud
   And defending the poor;
   Then humbled Himself
   To death on a cross,
   To crush the oppressor
   And rescue the lost.

4. The Light of the World
   Still shines on the earth,
   With gifts of forgiveness,
   The hope of new birth.
   So open your heart,
   Don't hide in the night;
   Step out of the darkness
   And into His light.

There is an everlasting kindness
(The compassion hymn)

Is 25:4; 52:7; 53:4; Mt 8:3; 9:36; 27:29; Mk 10:14; Lk 23:43; Rom 12:1; Eph 1:8; Heb 1:3

Keith & Kristyn Getty and Stuart Townend

♩ = 92

With a slight swing

Verse

1. There is an e-ver-last-ing kind-ness You la-vished on us, when the ra-diance of hea-ven came to re-scue the lost. You called the sheep with-out a shep-herd to leave their dis-tress, for Your streams of for-give-ness and the shade of Your rest.

1. shade of Your rest.

2. And with com-

2. And with compassion for the hurting You reached out Your hand,
   As the lame ran to meet You and the dead breathed again.
   You saw behind the eyes of sorrow and shared in our tears;
   Heard the sigh of the weary, let the children draw near.

3. We stood beneath the cross of Calvary and gazed on Your face,
   At the thorns of oppression and the wounds of disgrace;
   For surely You have borne our suffering and carried our grief,
   As You pardoned the scoffer and showed grace to the thief.

4. How beautiful the feet that carry this gospel of peace
   To the fields of injustice and the valleys of need;
   To be a voice of hope and healing, to answer the cries
   Of the hungry and helpless with the mercy of Christ.

To see the King of heaven fall

(Gethsemane)

Mk 14:35-36, 50; 15:34;
Heb 5:7; 1 Jn 4:10

Keith Getty & Stuart Townend

2. To know each friend will fall away,
And heaven's voice be still,
For hell to have its vengeful day
Upon Golgotha's hill.
No words describe the Saviour's plight,
To be by God forsaken
Till wrath and love are satisfied,
And every sin is paid,
And every sin is paid.

3. What took Him to this wretched place,
What kept Him on this road?
His love for Adam's curséd race,
For every broken soul.
No sin too slight to overlook,
No crime too great to carry,
All mingled in this poisoned cup,
And yet He drank it all
The Saviour drank it all,
The Saviour drank it all.

STORY BEHIND THE SONG
TO SEE THE KING OF HEAVEN FALL (GETHSEMANE)

As with most of the songs I have written with Keith Getty, *Gethsemane* started with a melody he sent me. We had discussed many times our desire to write songs that narrated and explored particular moments in the life of Christ, and I felt this melody had a particular haunting depth and power, and I began to think about that night before Jesus' death, spent praying in the Garden of Gethsemane.

It's a moment in His life that we may tend to gloss over, or perhaps even be a little perplexed by: Why was the prospect of the cross so terrible to Him? OK, nobody wants to die horribly, but many before and since have gone to martyrdom with a song on their lips. What was the root of Christ's anguish?

I had a few years before heard a powerful explanation from C.J. Mahaney: at the core of His suffering was not the prospect of death; it was the prospect of bearing the weight and the curse of every sin that has ever been committed, and its dreadful consequence – complete and utter separation from His loving Father. A place of such darkness, such isolation, such evil, such torture, that words and thoughts cannot begin to describe it. And yet that's what the Son of God chose to suffer – for us.

Viewed in this light, it becomes an important part of understanding the unfathomable depths of His sacrifice, and the true cost of the cross.

Speak, O Lord

Mt 5:16; Rom 1:5; 12:2; 2 Cor 9:13;
Eph 3:18; Gal 3:11; Heb 5:12; Jas 2:18

Keith Getty & Stuart Townend

1. Speak, O Lord, as we come to You to receive the food of Your holy word.

Take Your truth, plant it deep in us; shape and

Coda

glo - ry,—   with Your glo - ry.—

2. Teach us Lord full obedience,
   Holy reverence, true humility.
   Test our thoughts and our attitudes
   In the radiance of Your purity.
   Cause our faith to rise,
   Cause our eyes to see
   Your majestic love and authority.
   Words of power that can never fail;
   Let their truth prevail over unbelief.

3. Speak, O Lord, and renew our minds;
   Help us grasp the heights of Your plans for us.
   Truths unchanged from the dawn of time,
   That will echo down through eternity.
   And by grace we'll stand on Your promises;
   And by faith we'll walk as You walk with us.
   Speak, O Lord, till Your church is built
   And the earth is filled with Your glory,
   With Your glory.

O Church, arise

Is 53:10; Mt 22:44; 25:21, 23;
1 Cor 15:25; 2 Cor 4:8; 12:10;
Eph 6:13-14, 16-17; Phil 3:14;
Heb 12:1; Rev 1:7

Stuart Townend & Keith Getty

♩ = 70

1. O Church, a - rise, and put your ar - mour on; hear the call of Christ our Cap - tain. For now the weak can say that they are strong in the strength that God has giv - en. With shield of faith and belt of truth, we'll stand a - gainst the de - vil's lies; an ar - my bold, whose bat - tle - cry is Love, reach - ing

out to those in darkness. 2. Our call to -tions. Oh,-

oh,— oh,— oh,— oh,— — 3. Come, see the

2. Our call to war, to love the captive soul
   But to rage against the captor;
   And with the sword that makes the wounded whole,
   We will fight with faith and valour.
   When faced with trials on every side
   We know the outcome is secure,
   And Christ will have the prize for which He died,
   An inheritance of nations.

3. Come see the cross, where love and mercy meet,
   As the Son of God is stricken;
   Then see His foes lie crushed beneath His feet,
   For the Conqueror has risen!
   And as the stone is rolled away,
   And Christ emerges from the grave,
   This victory march continues till the day
   Every eye and heart shall see Him.

4. So Spirit, come, put strength in every stride,
   Give grace for every hurdle,
   That we may run with faith to win the prize
   Of a servant good and faithful.
   As saints of old still line the way,
   Retelling triumphs of His grace,
   We hear their calls, and hunger for the day
   When with Christ we stand in glory.

My heart is filled with thankfulness

Ps 69:30;
Is 53:4; Jer 31:33;
Lk 24:15; 2 Cor 12:10; Gal 3:13

Stuart Townend & Keith Getty

1. My— heart is filled with thank-ful-ness to Him who bore my pain; who— plumbed the depths of my dis-grace and gave me life a-gain.— who— crushed my curse of sin-ful-ness, and clothed me in His light,— and— wrote His law of right-eous-ness with pow'r up-on my heart.

2. My heart is filled with thankfulness
To Him who walks beside;
Who floods my weaknesses with strength
And causes fears to fly;
Whose every promise is enough
For every step I take,
Sustaining me with arms of love
And crowning me with grace.

3. My heart is filled with thankfulness
To Him who reigns above;
Whose wisdom is my perfect peace,
Whose every thought is love.
For every day I have on earth
Is given by the King.
So I will give my life, my all,
To love and follow Him.

Holy Spirit, living Breath of God

Gen 1:2; Jn 17:21; 20:22; Acts 13:52;
Rom 12:1; Phil 4:5; Col 3:12, 16;
Heb 11:1; 1 Pet 4:8; Rev 5:8; 8:4

Capo 1(D)

Keith Getty & Stuart Townend

May 2016

1. Holy Spirit, living Breath of God, breathe new life into my willing soul. Bring the presence of the risen Lord, to renew my heart and make me whole.

Cause Your word to come a - live in me; give me faith for what I
can - not see, give me pas-sion for Your pu - ri - ty; Ho - ly
Spi - rit, breathe new life in see.

2. Holy Spirit, come abide within,
   May Your joy be seen in all I do.
   Love enough to cover every sin,
   In each thought and deed and attitude.
   Kindness to the greatest and the least,
   Gentleness that sows the path of peace.
   Turn my strivings into works of grace;
   Breath of God, show Christ in all I do.

3. Holy Spirit, from creation's birth,
   Giving life to all that God has made,
   Show Your power once again on earth,
   Cause Your church to hunger for Your ways.
   Let the fragrance of our prayers arise;
   Lead us on the road of sacrifice,
   That in unity the face of Christ
   May be clear for all the world to see.

OTHER HYMNS AND SONGS

Inevitably in any collection some pieces refuse to be categorised! That is the case with the following group of songs and hymns – usually because for one reason or another I have never got round to recording them. However, my writing partner Keith Getty and his wife Kristyn are jointly responsible for many of them, and have recorded them on their own albums.

My collaboration with Keith goes back to 2000, when we were introduced by a mutual friend at a conference, resulting in Keith sending me some melodies on a CD – the first one of which became *In Christ alone*!

Keith has a unique ability to produce melodies that are singable and memorable, yet carry an extraordinary emotional power and timeless quality.

Since then we have written dozens of pieces together, some quite deliberately filling a perceived gap in the canon of songs and hymns used in the church today. And it has been great to see our working relationship develop – almost always beginning with a melody idea from Keith, which we then work on and help to shape together, and then me working on lyric ideas which he filters and critiques thematically and poetically. It's a true collaboration, based on mutual respect for each other's gifts, always honest, and most of the time great fun!

It is mainly through my work with Keith (and more recently also with Kristyn) that the label of 'hymn-writer' has begun to stick. However, my first 'hymn' was written some years before, when a simple melody popped into my head one day while I was considering the cost of the Father giving up His Son for my sake. *How deep the Father's love* was the result – an accident, really, but one that has helped set my writing in a direction I never planned to go.

Why write hymns? Well, I enjoy the challenge for one thing! Writing within a more formal structure of rhythmic patterns and rhyming schemes forces you to work hard at the words; although sometimes you feel you're fighting the genre for control of the meaning and you mustn't let the rhymes write the song or let the scansion reduce you to highfaluting banalities!

But it's more than just a personal challenge. When you get it right, the form and the language join with the content to bring a more profound revelation of who God is. As someone once said, 'The mystery of God is so deep, sometimes only poetry will do!' And I'm encouraged that our poetry-packed Bibles seem to concur with that statement.

By faith, we see the hand of God

Mt 17:20; 28:19;
Lk 4:18; Acts 1:8;
2 Cor 5:7; Phil 4:13; Heb 11:3, 13; 12:2

Capo 3(G)

♩= 76

Keith & Kristyn Getty and Stuart Townend

1. By faith, we see the hand of God in the light of cre-a-tion's grand de-sign; in the lives of those who prove His faith-ful-ness, who walk by faith and not by sight.

reign. We will stand as chil-dren of the

1.,3.
D.C.(v.2/v.4)

2.,4.,5.

Chorus

197

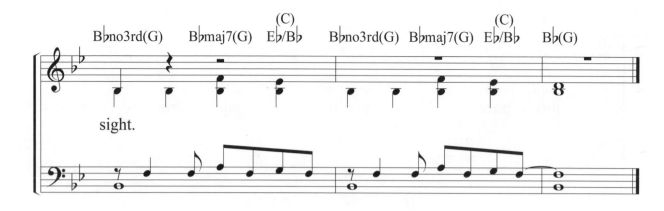

sight.

2. By faith, our fathers roamed the earth
   With the power of His promise in their hearts
   Of a holy city built by God's own hand –
   A place where peace and justice reign.

3. By faith, the prophets saw a day
   When the longed-for Messiah would appear
   With the power to break the chains of sin and death,
   And rise triumphant from the grave.

4. By faith, the church was called to go
   In the power of the Spirit to the lost
   To deliver captives and to preach good news
   In every corner of the earth.

5. By faith, this mountain shall be moved,
   And the power of the gospel shall prevail,
   For we know in Christ all things are possible
   For those who call upon His name.

Father, we have sinned

Ps 106:6; Lk 6:20; 15:21

(Repentance)

Stuart Townend & Keith Getty

1. Fa-ther, we have sinned in word, and deed, and thought, through ig-no-rance, through weak-ness, through de-li-b'rate fault: we've sinned a-gainst our neigh-bours and a-gainst You, Lord, yet we are tru-ly sor-ry, and we turn to You once more.

2. Father of the nations, You who bless the poor,
   We're servants of the endless want and drive for more.
   We've made our greed a virtue, while the children starve,
   Come, change our joy to sorrow, till our lives reflect Your heart.

Fullness of grace

Is 53:3, 5, 10; Mt 1:19; Lk 1:34; 2:7; Jn 1:14; Rom 5:19; 2 Cor 4:6; Phil 2:7; Col 1:19; 2:9; 1 Pet 1:8

Capo 3 (Bm)

Keith & Kristyn Getty
& Stuart Townend

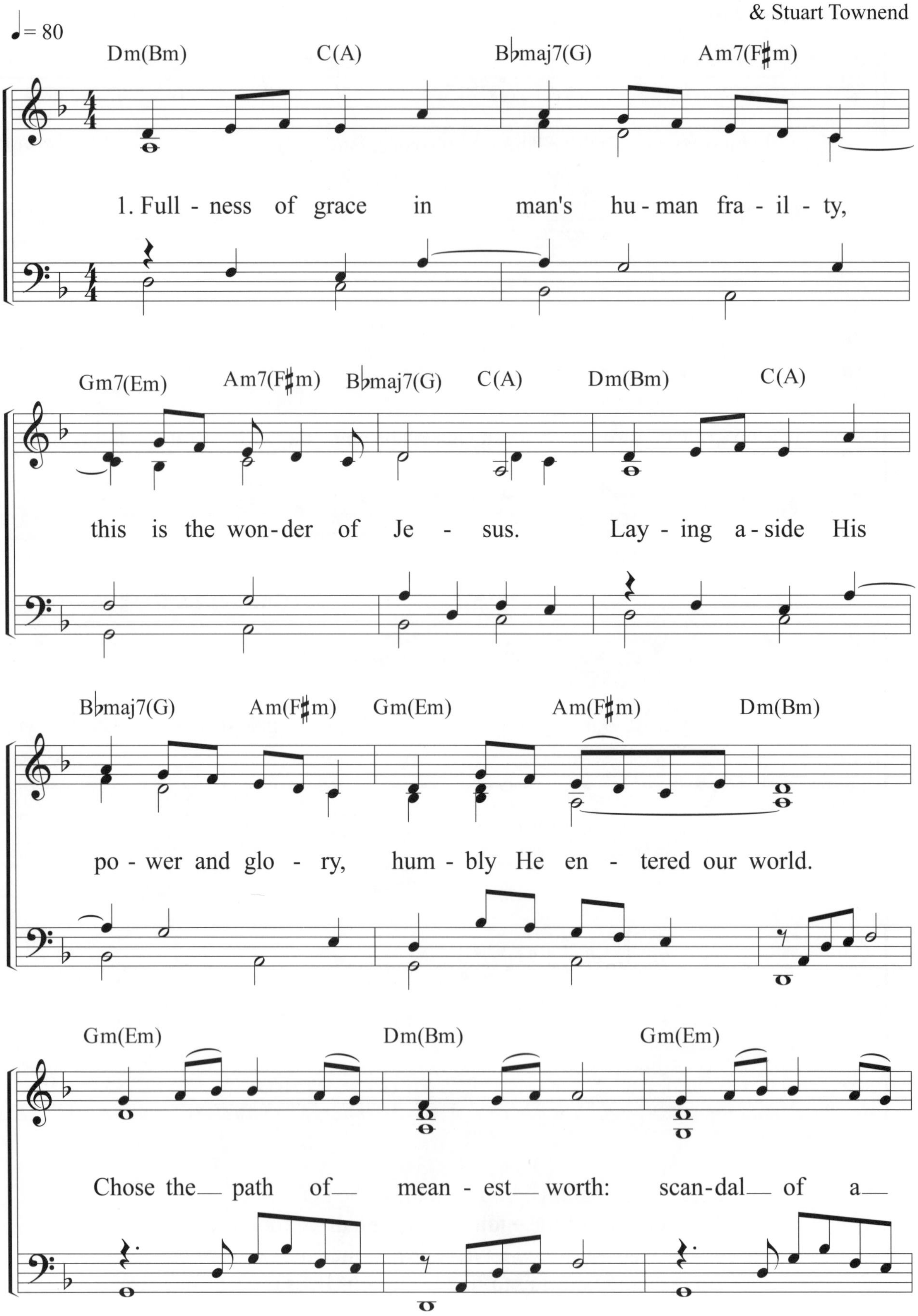

♩= 80
Dm(Bm) C(A) B♭maj7(G) Am7(F♯m)
1. Full - ness of grace in man's hu - man fra - il - ty,
Gm7(Em) Am7(F♯m) B♭maj7(G) C(A) Dm(Bm) C(A)
this is the won - der of Je - sus. Lay - ing a - side His
B♭maj7(G) Am(F♯m) Gm(Em) Am(F♯m) Dm(Bm)
po - wer and glo - ry, hum - bly He en - tered our world.
Gm(Em) Dm(Bm) Gm(Em)
Chose the path of mean - est worth: scan - dal of a

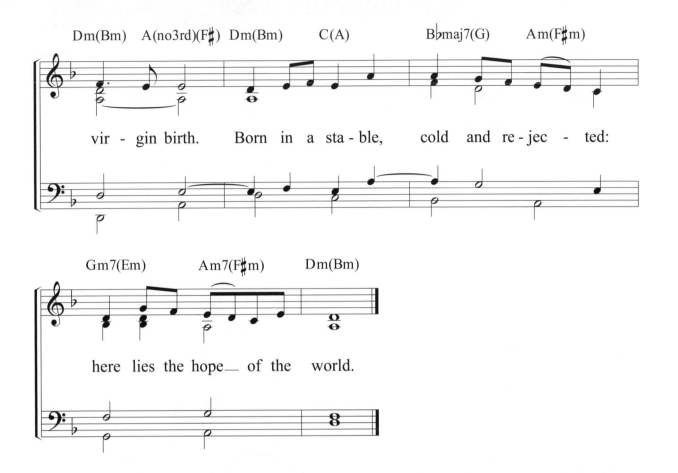

vir - gin birth.   Born in a sta - ble,   cold   and re - jec - ted:

here lies the hope___ of the   world.

2. Fullness of grace, the love of the Father
Shown in the face of Jesus.
Stooping to bear the weight of humanity,
Walking the Calvary road.
Christ the holy Innocent
Took our sin and punishment.
Fullness of God, despised and rejected:
Crushed for the sins of the world.

3. Fullness of hope in Christ we had longed for,
Promise of God in Jesus.
Through His obedience we are forgiven,
Opening the floodgates of heaven.
All our hopes and dreams we bring
Gladly as an offering.
Fullness of life and joy unspeakable:
God's gift in love to the world.

Giver of grace
(You are good to me)

Ps 13:6; 61:3; 62:2; 119:72;
Ezek 34:26; Jn 1:17; Eph 1:7-8, 14; 2:6

Stuart Townend

1. Giv-er of grace,— how price-less Your love— for— me,
pur-er than sil - ver, more cost-ly than gold.— Giv-er of life,—
all that I'll ev - er— need, strength for my bo - dy and
food for my soul.— Oh, You are good, so
good to me. Yes, You are good, so good to me.—Oh, You are

good, so good to me. Yes, You are good, so

good to me.___ I've ne-ver known___ a love___ so

per-fect in___ its faith - ful-ness;___ it lifts me up to the high -

- est place. A glimpse of hea-ven and___ a

taste of my___ in - he - ri-tance,___ I know that one day I'll be___

D.C.(v.1) al fine

___ with You.

2. Giver of hope, Rock of salvation,
Tower of refuge, yet there in my pain.
Now I'm secure, loved for eternity,
Showered with blessings
And lavished with grace.

203

Jesus is Lord

Mt 28:6; Lk 15:20; Jn 1:1; 6:51; 13:5;
Acts 2:24; Rom 10:9; Gal 3:13; Eph 1:7;
Phil 2:7, 10; 1 Thess 4:17; Rev 1:7

Stuart Townend & Keith Getty

2. Jesus is Lord – whose voice sustains the stars and planets,
   Yet in His wisdom laid aside His crown.
   Jesus the Man, who washed our feet, who bore our suffering,
   Became a curse to bring salvation's plan.

3. Jesus is Lord – the tomb is gloriously empty!
   Not even death could crush this King of love!
   The price is paid, the chains are loosed, and we're forgiven,
   And we can run into the arms of God.

4. 'Jesus is Lord' – a shout of joy, a cry of anguish,
   As He returns, and every knee bows low.
   Then every eye and every heart will see His glory,
   The Judge of all will take His children home.

Joy has dawned upon the world

Mt 1:23; 2:1, 11;
Lk 2:5-9; 1 Cor 15:47;
2 Cor 5:19; Heb 10:20

Capo 1(D)

Stuart Townend & Keith Getty

1. Joy has dawned up-on the world, pro-mised from cre-a - tion: God's sal-va-tion now un-furled, hope for e-v'ry na-tion. Not with fan-fares from a-bove,

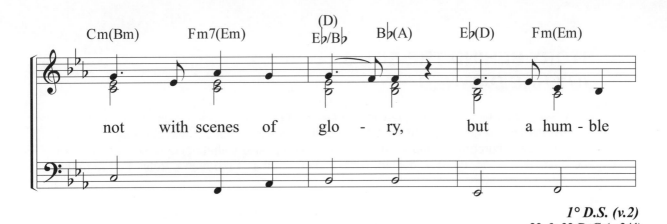

not with scenes of glo - ry, but a hum - ble

1° D.S. (v.2)
2° & 3° D.C.(v.3/4)
4° D.S.S.
5° D.C. al fine

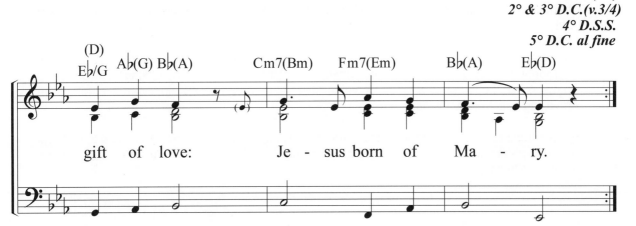

gift of love: Je - sus born of Ma - ry.

2. Sounds of wonder fill the sky
   With the songs of angels,
   As the mighty Prince of Life
   Shelters in a stable.
   Hands that set each star in place,
   Shaped the earth in darkness,
   Cling now to a mother's breast,
   Vulnerable and helpless.

3. Shepherds bow before the Lamb,
   Gazing at the glory;
   Gifts of men from distant lands
   Prophesy the story.
   Gold, a King is born today,
   Incense, God is with us,
   Myrrh, His death will make a way,
   And by His blood He'll win us.

4. Son of Adam, Son of heaven,
   Given as a ransom,
   Reconciling God and man,
   Christ our mighty Champion!
   What a Saviour, what a Friend,
   What a glorious mystery:
   Once a babe in Bethlehem,
   Now the Lord of history.

STORY BEHIND THE SONG
JOY HAS DAWNED

Keith Getty and I wrote *Joy has dawned* as part of a project we worked on of a collection of new hymns and songs based on the themes of the Apostles' Creed. Keith and I both share a passion to see churches singing songs full of truth; compositions that not only express our love and devotion to God, but also declare the wonderful truths of the faith – truths that form the foundation of our lives.

With that in mind, we realised that there was a shortage of new material on a number of key themes – one being the incarnation. We therefore set about trying to write what is essentially a Christmas carol, telling the story and significance of Christ's birth, and this is the result.

There are parts of the Christmas story that are so familiar to us, we tend not to appreciate how extraordinary they are: the humble circumstances of the birth of the King of kings; His choosing to come into the world as a helpless, vulnerable baby; the prophetic significance of gifts from travelling astrologers; the list goes on…

It's a song that lends itself to a variety of musical styles, from a worship band setting to a choral piece, perhaps even a Salvation Army band arrangement, and I hope it's a useful addition to a church's Christmas repertoire.

Lord, we wait

Capo 1 (D)

Stuart Townend & Keith Getty

Stately

1. Lord, we wait for the day of Your ap - pear - ing; Lord, we wait for Your com-ing in the clouds. With a shout the trum-pet will___ sound, and the dead will be raised to___ life, and we shall meet Him in the air!

2. In that day death is swallowed up in victory;
In that day sin and death will be no more.

3. Now in part – we see shadows of His glory;
Then in full – we shall see Him face to face!

King of the ages

Jn 8:12; Acts 13:47;
Col 1:27; Rev 1:7; 15:3-4

Stuart Townend & Keith Getty

Majestically

me, bring-ing peace and the hope of glo-ry.

2. Your arms of love are reaching out
   To every soul that seeks You;
   Your light will shine in all the earth,
   Bringing grace and a great salvation.

3. The day will come when You appear,
   And every eye shall see You.
   Then we shall rise with hearts ablaze,
   With a song we will sing forever.

Love of God

Is 9:6; Mt 13:46; Lk 15:20;
Gal 3:29; Eph 3:19; Phil 2:7

Keith Getty & Stuart Townend

2. Love of God, revealed in frailty,
   Through the gift of a servant King;
   Joy of heaven robed in humility,
   Prince of Peace crowned with suffering.
   Oh, what love that calls humanity
   To kneel at the cross,
   And exchange our sin's futility
   For the joy of a father's love.

3. Love of God, what priceless treasure
   Over all this world affords:
   To be His and His forever,
   This my glory and my reward!
   May this love beyond all knowing,
   So capture my soul
   That I'm filled to overflowing
   With a passion for Him alone!

Merciful God

Ex 34:6; Ps 86:5, 15;
Heb 8:12; Jude 24

Keith & Kristyn Getty
& Stuart Townend

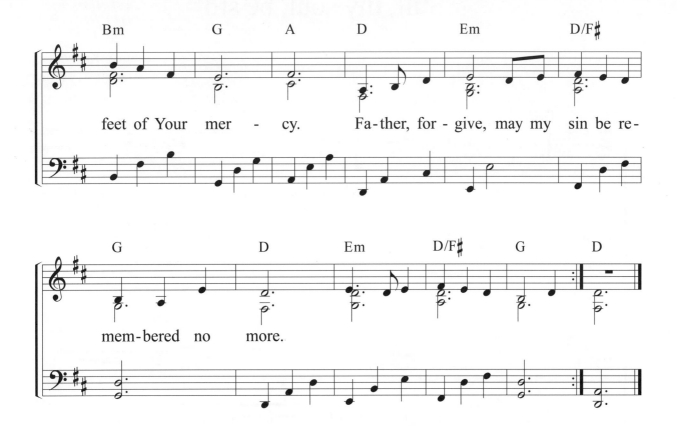

feet of Your mer - cy. Fa-ther, for - give, may my sin be re-

mem-bered no more.

2. Merciful God, O abounding in love,
   Faithful through times we have failed You –
   Selfish in thought and uncaring in deed,
   Foolish in word and ungrateful.
   Spirit of God, conquer our hearts
   With love that flows from forgiveness;
   Cause us to yield and return to the mercy of God.

3. Merciful God, O abounding in love,
   Faithful to keep us from falling,
   Guiding our ways with Your fatherly heart,
   Growing our faith with each testing.
   God speed the day struggles will end,
   Faultless we'll gaze on Your glory;
   Then we will stand overwhelmed by the mercy of God.

Still, my soul, be still

Ps 31:14; 51:10; 62:1, 5;
Eph 6:16; 2 Thess 2:15;
2 Pet 1:19; 1 Jn 2:24

Keith & Kristyn Getty
& Stuart Townend

trust in You and not be sha - ken. Lord___ of peace, re-

- new a stead-fast spi-rit with-in me to rest in You a-

lone.

2. Still, my soul, be still,
   Do not be moved
   By lesser lights and fleeting shadows.
   Hold on to His ways,
   With shield of faith
   Against temptation's flaming arrows.

3. Still, my soul, be still,
   Do not forsake
   The truth you learned in the beginning.
   Wait upon the Lord,
   And hope will rise
   As stars appear when day is dimming.

We are heirs of God Almighty

(Trinity hymn)

Capo 3 (G)

Tune: AUSTRIA

Deut 32:9-10; Mt 5:14; Jn 14:16; 15:5; Gal 5:22; Eph 1:4, 13-14; Phil 1:6, 10-11; 3:10; Titus 2:11-12

Franz Joseph Haydn (1732-1809)

Triumphantly

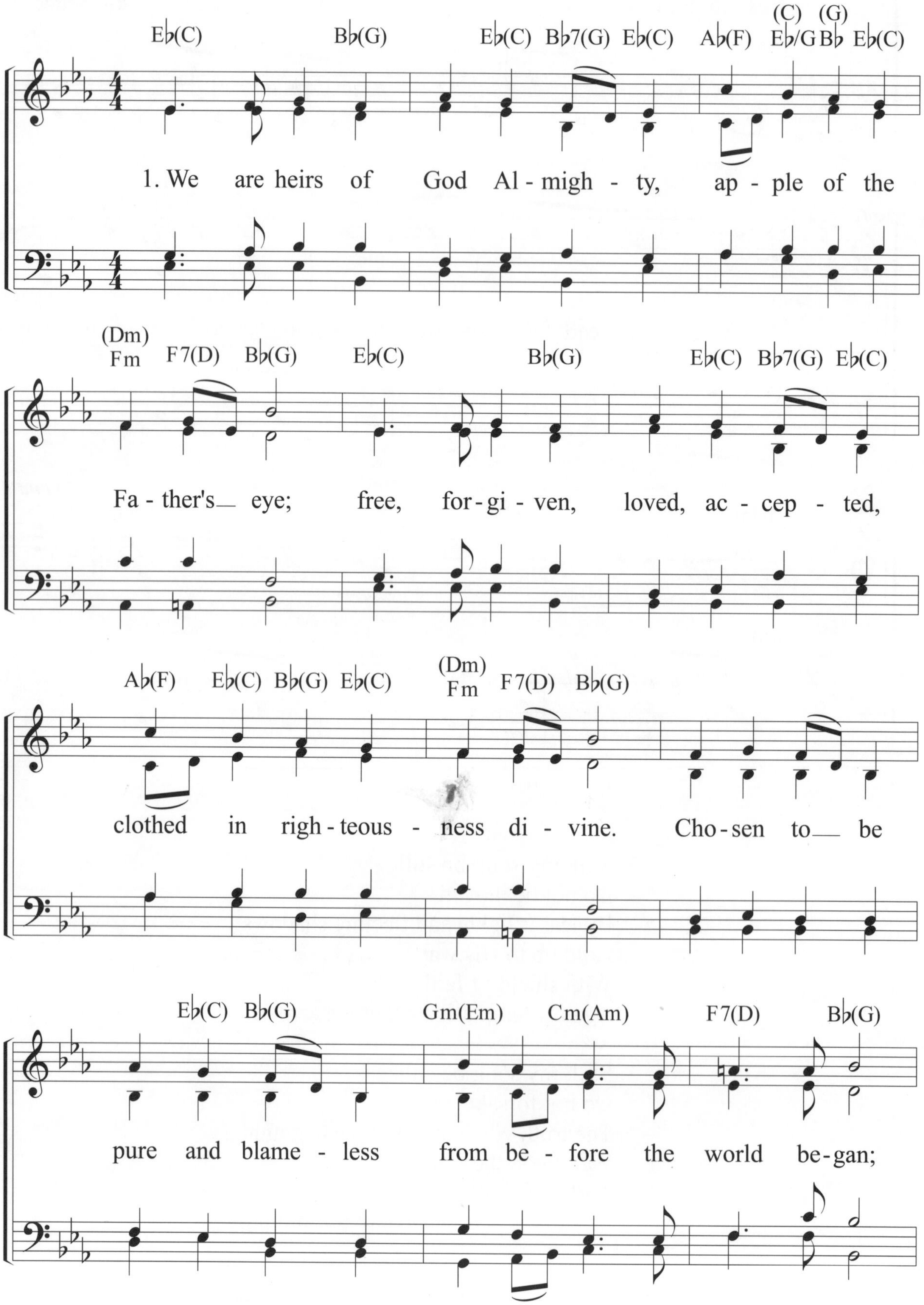

E♭(C) B♭(G) E♭(C) B♭7(G) E♭(C) A♭(F) (C) (G) E♭/G B♭ E♭(C)
1. We are heirs of God Al-migh-ty, ap-ple of the
(Dm) Fm F7(D) B♭(G) E♭(C) B♭(G) E♭(C) B♭7(G) E♭(C)
Fa-ther's_ eye; free, for-gi-ven, loved, ac-cep-ted,
A♭(F) E♭(C) B♭(G) E♭(C) (Dm) Fm F7(D) B♭(G)
clothed in righ-teous-ness di-vine. Cho-sen to_ be
E♭(C) B♭(G) Gm(Em) Cm(Am) F7(D) B♭(G)
pure and blame-less from be-fore the world be-gan;

grace for ev - 'ry si - tu - a - tion, shel - tered _ in _ the _

Fa - ther's _ hand.

2. We have Christ at work within us,
Shaping us to be like Him;
Resurrection power sustaining
Freedom from the snares of sin.
Saying no to flesh desires,
Saying yes to righteous ways;
Filled with passion and with power,
Lights that burn in darkened days.

3. We've the Spirit without measure,
Helper, Comforter and Guide;
One who brings the gifts of heaven,
One who comes to walk beside.
Taste of heaven's endless pleasure,
Guarantee of what's to come;
Causing fruit to grow in action,
Bringing glory to the Son.

Stuart Townend

We've come to praise You

Rom 8:32; Rev 19:11

Capo 2(E/F)

Kate Simmonds & Stuart Townend

We've come to praise You, 'cause You're wor-thy. No-bo-dy like You in Your glo-ry. We love to praise You, 'cause You're ho-ly, awe-some, won-der-ful, migh-ty God.

(repeat 1st time only)

And ev-'ry-thing that You do

221

Who paints the skies?
(River of fire)

Gen 30:22; Ps 79:13; Is 64:8;
Ezek 11:19; 36:26; Dan 7:10;
Jn 1:3; Rev 5:9; 14:6

Stuart Townend

♩ = 115

Verse

(Call) 1. { Who paints___ the skies in - to glo - rious___ day?___
Who shapes___ the val - leys___ and brings the___ rain?___ }

(Response) On - ly___ the splen-dour___ of Je - sus.

(Call) { Who breathes___ His life in - to
Who makes___ the de - sert___ to

fists of clay?___
live a - gain?___ } (Response) On - ly___ the splen-dour___ of Je - sus.

Teach ev - 'ry na-tion___ His mar-v'llous ways;___

each ge - ne - ra-tion_ shall sing His praise.___

Chorus

He_ is won-der - ful, He_ is glo-ri - ous, clothed_ in righ-teous - ness,

full__ of ten - der - ness. Come__ and wor - ship_ Him,

He's_ the Prince of_ life, He_ will cleanse our_ hearts in_ His ri-ver_ of

fire.

2. Who hears the cry of the barren one?
Only the mercy of Jesus.
Who breaks the curse of the heart of stone?
Only the mercy of Jesus.
Who storms the prison and sets men free,
Only the mercy of Jesus.
Purchasing souls for eternity?
Only the mercy of Jesus.

DISCOGRAPHY

 Say the Word (1997)

 Personal Worship (1999)

 Lord of Every Heart (2002)

 Monument to Mercy (2006)

 The Best of Stuart Townend Live (2007)

 There is a Hope (2008)

 Creation Sings (2009)

Index of Titles and First Lines

Authors' titles, where different from first lines, are shown in *italics*.

CD-ROM CONTENTS

SATB Arrangements

All my days *(Beautiful Saviour)*
Behold the Lamb *(The Communion hymn)*
Come, people of the risen King
Creation sings the Father's song
Father, we have sinned *(Repentance)*
From the breaking of the dawn *(Every Promise)*
Hear the call of the kingdom
How deep the Father's love for us
In Christ alone
Jesus is Lord
Joy has dawned
King of the ages
Let the earth resound
Lord, we wait
Love of God
May the peace of God *(Benediction)*
My heart is filled with thankfulness
O Church, arise
Oh, to see the dawn *(The power of the cross)*
See what a morning *(Resurrection hymn)*
Speak, O Lord
Spirit of heaven
The Lord's my Shepherd *(Psalm 23)*
There is a hope
To see the King of heaven fall *(Gethsemane)*
We are heirs of God Almighty *(Trinity hymn)*
When Love came down to earth
You're the Word of God the Father *(Across the lands)*

**Monument to Mercy
standard sheet music**

In every day that dawns *(I'm grateful)*
From the breaking of the dawn *(Every Promise)*
Knowing Your grace *(Child of the King)*
The Lord's my Shepherd *(Psalm 23)*
What love has captured me? *(Filled with wonder)*
Belovèd and Blessèd
Oh, to see the dawn *(The power of the cross)*
See what a morning *(Resurrection hymn)*

Scriptural Reference Index

Song & Hymn Texts